HAUNTED
LIVERPOOL 9

© Tom Slemen 2004

Edited by Claire Walker
Published by The Bluecoat Press, Liverpool
Book design by March Design, Liverpool
Printed by Ashford Colour Press, Gosport

ISBN 1 872568 80 7

Tom Slemen
HAUNTED
LIVERPOOL 9

The Bluecoat Press

Contents

Dancing Devils

Many years ago, I was browsing through a second-hand bookshop in Wales when I came across a book that contained the handwritten reminiscences of a Dr Wolfe, who had once had a medical practice in Victorian Liverpool. The conversations which take place between a doctor and a patient in his surgery should remain as confidential as those between a priest and a parishioner in a confessional. However, Dr Wolfe wrote a tract about a bizarre and eerie case concerning one of his patients, decades after his death. Why he wrote the tract has never been determined, but it was certainly never intended for publication.

In the summer of 1884, Richard Maddox, a sixty-five-year-old businessman of Kent Square, in south Liverpool, started to experience alarming hallucinations. These troubling phantasms of his mind first materialised one evening in March, 1884, as Mr Maddox was smoking an after-dinner pipe in his drawing room. The maid had got a roaring fire going in the room and had just brought in some fresh logs. As she was about to leave, Maddox called her back and asked if she too could hear the sound of children's laughter. The maid stood still and listened intently for a few moments, but could hear nothing and soon took leave of her master.

Several minutes after the maid had left the room, a terrifying incident took place. Maddox had gone over to the window to see if there were any children playing in the street, although the laughter seemed to come from inside the room itself. Suddenly, a lurid green radiance flooded the room and turned everything in it a sickly shade of green. He spun round, and was confronted by five small, luminous, green devils, each about two feet in height, dancing and cavorting around the room. The peculiar visitants danced in formation with synchronised movements, and they all gabbled away simultaneously in a strange, unintelligible language, interspersed with high-pitched, childlike laughter. Maddox was naturally appalled by what he saw, and flung his pipe at the sinister apparitions, then ran out of the drawing room in terror.

The maid and another servant listened politely to their employer's account of the green devils and the peculiar green light, but their faces betrayed the fact that they doubted the truth of what he was telling them. In fact, it was obvious to Maddox that they thought he had lost his sanity. Nevertheless, to humour him, they agreed to follow him into the drawing room to see for themselves. When they entered the room they found nothing supernatural at all, only their master's smoking pipe where it had landed on the carpet.

This was not to be a one off incident and Maddox ended up being plagued by the weird, mischievous, glowing imps to such an extent that he was advised by a relative to consult Dr Wolfe, who had been a friend of the family for many years.

Wolfe's initial response, after listening to the far-fetched tale, was to suspect Maddox of abusing alcohol, or hallucinogenic drugs. He said that he knew of a 'blue devils' phenomenon experienced by alcoholics suffering from delirium tremens – the 'DTs' – but Maddox truthfully insisted that he only enjoyed the occasional glass of port. Wolfe then probed further, asking his patient if he took opiates or any other kind of drug, upon which Maddox assured him that he smoked nothing more potent than tobacco. For good measure, when questioned about his lifestyle, he was able to insist that he had not been under any unusual stress of any kind, and that he regularly enjoyed eight hours of sound sleep.

Having ruled out substance abuse and any type of anxiety disorder, Wolfe then wondered if Maddox's mind was succumbing to the early onset of senile dementia, yet his patient seemingly had his full mental faculties intact, and was renowned throughout the city as being a very astute businessman.

Therefore, finding himself at a loss as to a diagnosis, Dr Wolfe suggested a fortnight of complete rest in the countryside, and Maddox readily took the advice, if only to be away from the source of his troubles for a while. The two weeks were blissful; not once was Maddox persecuted by the visions of the horned green gremlins. Even when he was back home it was the same. Before setting off for the country, Maddox had taken the opportunity of arranging to have his drawing room redecorated. The work was not quite finished by the time he returned and for a few days he had to take his after-dinner pipe in the back parlour. After one of these smoking sessions he wrote to Dr Wolfe, thanking him for his good advice, which had apparently worked wonders.

However, a few days later, the work on the drawing room was finally completed and Maddox surveyed the finished room with satisfaction. After puffing on his customary pipe, he had settled down to read a book, in his favourite armchair by the drawing room fire. He felt so relaxed in these comfortable surroundings and breathed a long sigh of relief. His recent ordeal seemed to be over and his peaceful routine had once again been restored.

Then, suddenly, the dreaded dancing devils reappeared out of nowhere and encircled him. They once again danced around him menacingly, gibbering in their strange diabolical tongue, giggling and laughing; obviously deriving some hideous kind of pleasure from the poor man's torment. Maddox felt his heart beat wildly in his chest as he let out a strangled cry and gripped the arms of the chair in terror. The commotion brought all the servants running to see what had happened, but, once again, they could see nothing unusual in the room – only their master, rigid, white-faced and terrified, clinging to the arms of his chair.

The accursed green visitors continued to plague Maddox whenever he entered the accursed drawing room, putting a severe strain on his nerves. His once ruddy complexion took on a pale, waxy hue and his eyes darted about anxiously. His once sturdy frame seemed to shrink and he was soon reduced to a mere shadow of the man he had once been and he would jump nervously at the slightest noise. His decline continued and within a year he died from a stroke.

After the funeral, Maddox's relatives gathered at his house to lament his untimely death. One of them noticed that the curlicued brass fender around the fireplace was new and that it depicted, on its frontpiece, a head with a face like Pan, the old god of mischief. When questioned, no one in the house was able to say where the strange fender had come from, but one of the maids said that when the coals were lit inside that fender, strange green sparks were often seen.

Was that uncanny fender somehow connected with the tormenting devils that haunted Richard Maddox?

Stalking Skeletons

Another case of supernatural persecution also has a Liverpool connection. The notes of a Dr R Williams, published in a psychiatric journal in the 1920s, include the history of a wealthy, thirty-three-year-old Liverpool man, who is only identified as Mr Runcy.

In 1899, Runcy was living in the Knightsbridge area of London. He had inherited a large fortune and was therefore in the fortunate position of not having to work to support himself. One morning, in July 1899, he awoke with a fearful hangover after a night of hard-drinking with his companions. As Runcy sat up in bed, rubbing his head and squinting at the light filtering through the curtains, he noticed a strange black cat sitting on the carpet facing him. Its piercing eyes seemed to be of an almost luminous cobalt blue, and it sat staring intently at the man of leisure. Runcy was baffled, as he did not own a cat – he didn't particularly like animals – and so he surmised that one of his madcap friends had put the creature in the house as some kind of prank.

However, Runcy soon came to realise that the cat was no ordinary animal, as he was the only one who could see it; the maids, butlers, servants and cooks could not see any black cat, with or without glowing blue eyes, and neither could Runcy's friends.

Wherever Runcy went, the cat did too. He strolled through Hyde Park to try and rid himself of his hangover, and so did the hallucinatory cat. He visited a friend's home in Belgravia, and there was the cat, curled up on the rug, not taking his eyes off his quarry for a moment. Runcy tried to tell himself that the cat did not exist, that it was all some strange figment of his imagination, possibly brought about by the heavy drinking sessions in which he had been indulging, but all the same, the dreaded slinky black phantasm stalked him incessantly, until he was convinced that he was going insane.

Runcy confided in a close friend about the irksome vision, and this friend referred Runcy to Dr Williams, whose West End practice specialised in psychiatric illnesses. Dr Williams ordered Runcy to cease his life of debauchery at once. The all-night parties, the absinthe sprees, the outsized cigars, the rich exotic food and the womanising were to be replaced by a month of total rest and abstinence. Runcy was told to eat simple, bland food and to be in bed by no later than ten o'clock each night.

So worried was the young libertine, that he followed the doctor's orders to the letter and, in doing so, incurred the ridicule of his hellfire friends. However, within a week, the black cat had vanished and Runcy was so relieved that he went to thank Dr Williams in person, after which he returned to his Knightsbridge home with a new spring in his step.

However, his new-found peace of mind was to be short-lived, because as he was walking up the long hallway towards the stairs – a strange-looking man in eighteenth century clothing greeted him. The man wore a small white wig with a ribbon bow tied to its pigtail, and a long crimson satin coat embroidered with an intricate floral design. His black velvet trousers went down as far as the knees, and below that he wore white stockings and a pair of shiny, square-buckled shoes. This outlandish figure beckoned the dumbstruck Runcy with a small sword, which he waved towards the stairs.

"Who the devil are you?" Runcy asked the stranger, but the stranger said nothing, and only smiled in reply.

Runcy soon discovered that the bizarre character – like the black cat – could not be perceived by anyone else, and like the cat, this apparition followed him about everywhere. When he retired to bed at night, Runcy would peep over his blankets and catch sight of the old-fashioned phantom standing to attention in the form of a silhouette against the curtains. In the morning, the figure would still be standing in the same position, waiting for Runcy to rise, ready to resume shadowing him wherever he should go.

Dr Williams was most concerned by the new 'ideoform' as he called it, and he arranged for Runcy to be hypnotised, but even hypnosis could not cancel out the imaginary tormenter. Little did Runcy or Williams know that the hallucinatory nuisance would soon be replaced by a truly terrifying apparition.

One Sunday evening, Runcy was walking quickly along Portland Place in the rain, desperately trying to shake off the eighteenth century apparition who accompanied him everywhere. Glancing back, Runcy noted with relief that the street was deserted. There was no sign of the man from his imagination. He rushed homeward, constantly looking over his shoulder and checking the road ahead, but the annoying follower was nowhere to be seen.

Runcy then enjoyed an entire three days free of the man in the white wig and was just beginning to regain his composure, when, on the fourth day, his freedom was shattered. He had ventured out to a theatre in Covent Garden, and sitting next to him was a beautiful woman named Lydia Ellen, a young lady who had many admirers. Runcy was paying little attention to the play, being otherwise occupied whispering sweet nothings into the lovely Lydia's ear, when something suddenly caught his eye. Standing in the central aisle of the theatre, close to the end seat of Runcy's row, stood a tall human skeleton. Runcy stared in horror at the latest apparition borne of his troubled mind. Lydia immediately noticed the look of horror on his face, and followed the line of his gaze to the central aisle – and saw nothing amiss. The skeleton's head slowly turned and faced Runcy; its black eye sockets seemed to penetrate his own and its teeth and jaw formed the frozen grin typical of a skull.

Runcy was so distracted by the skeleton that Lydia soon became irritated, and was convinced that her beau was eyeing some other lady in the auditorium. She was used to being the sole centre of attention and in the end, with a rustle of silk petticoats, she stormed out of the theatre in a huff. The skeletal creature of Runcy's psyche had completely ruined the evening.

Runcy jumped into a hansom cab outside the theatre – and so did the skeleton; its bones rattling horribly whenever it made the slightest movement. He dashed into his home ahead of the skeleton, and slammed the front door. He then breathlessly ordered a puzzled servant to bolt all the doors and windows in the house, but when Runcy reached the drawing room, he saw, to his horror, that the skeleton was already there, standing in front of the blazing fire with its fleshless bony hands clasped behind its curving spine.

Wherever Runcy went, the rattling skeleton followed, and even when Dr Williams suggested a trip abroad, the grotesque figure took the advice too. It stuck like glue to Runcy during his entire stay in Switzerland, stalking him up the highest mountains and across the deepest lakes.

There is no happy ending to this tale.

After almost a decade of persecution, Runcy ended up in a lunatic asylum, and it is said that he died in bedlam. Even upon his deathbed, he saw the grinning face of the skeleton peering between the faces of his family as they attended him in his final hours.

*

Are these two cases – the dancing devils and the stalking skeleton – simply examples of figments of the imagination overtaking minds weakened by some psychosis, or mental disorder – or did the persecuting entities have an independent existence of their own?

The Mouth of Hell

In a certain part of Liverpool, there are two women – both in their early fifties – named Agnes and Joan, who have been the best of friends ever since they were children.

In 1999, Joan met a man named Ray, and they got on like a house on fire. It was as if they had known one another for years. Agnes was very pleased for Joan, because Joan hadn't had a male companion in years – in fact, since her separation from her violent husband. That separation had shattered Joan's life and had left her with a deep emotional scars and a complete distrust of all men.

Ray started to come round to Joan's house on most days and the relationship went from strength to strength.

There was an elderly spinster who lived in the same street as Agnes and Joan, whose name was Phyllis. She had the unenviable reputation for being a nosy, interfering old busybody. The two friends used to smile whenever they saw her net curtains twitching. Nothing went on in that street that Phyllis didn't know about and she took a keen interest in Joan's new boyfriend.

One afternoon in 1999, Agnes was on her way to visit Joan, when she saw two men sitting in a car that was parked outside Joan's house. When Joan came to the door, the men drove off, which worried Agnes, who said they'd been looking at the house in a suspicious way. Agnes and Joan decided that the men were probably burglars, casing up the house, and Joan promised to be more vigilant than usual.

By now, Joan had started a part-time job as a barmaid in a local club, and yet she was still signing on at the local job centre. A week after starting the job at the club, two benefit fraud officers from the DSS visited the club and issued her with an ultimatum; either she could continue to work and face prosecution, or she could declare what she had earned and continue signing on. Joan had no choice but to declare the £45 which she had been paid so far.

A few months later, she had another visitor from the DSS, this time at her home. They told her that they had been informed that she was co-habiting with a man. Joan tried to look surprised and asked them what they meant. The DSS official said that, for two months, a series of benefit fraud officers had been watching her house, and had seen Ray enter the house each evening. Two other DSS officers, on the morning shift, had seen Ray leave Joan's house at around nine o'clock. Their records showed that these comings and goings had been going on seven days a week throughout the period of surveillance. Joan had to admit that Ray had moved in with her – and she hadn't informed the DSS. Someone had obviously tipped them off.

The news spread throughout the neighbourhood, and old Phyllis, the nosy parker of the street, started to avoid Joan. In the end, Joan collared Phyllis in the supermarket and accused her of grassing her up, and Agnes had to pull her away as she turned the air blue with swear words.

A few days later, Joan and Agnes were visited by a television licence officer. Neither of the women was found to have a current licence, but Agnes was only cautioned because her television set wasn't in working order, but Joan had to go to court and was fined.

That same week, someone put old Phyllis's windows in. There were no witnesses, but most of the neighbours were convinced that it was Joan's act of revenge.

Not long afterwards, Agnes was peeling some potatoes in the kitchen, when she clutched her stomach, doubled up in agony. She had been ignoring a hernia that had been troubling her for months and her bowel was now constricted. She was rushed straight to hospital, and Joan promised to look after the house while she lay in the surgical ward, waiting to be operated upon.

Shortly afterwards, while Joan was minding Agnes's house, she was joined by her nephew Danny. After chatting for a while, Danny became bored and turned on Agnes's computer. Joan told him to leave the computer alone, but then Danny showed her something very interesting. On the computer screen – written on her word processor – were copies of letters she'd written – and emails she'd sent. There were several emails to the DSS, informing them that Joan was working as a barmaid while still claiming benefit – and one about Joan cohabiting with a man. One email was to the TV Licensing Authority's website – informing them that Joan had no television licence. Agnes had even told the licence people to visit her own house – knowing that her own television was broken and beyond repair. One letter, which had been written sixteen months ago, told a certain electricity company that Joan's electricity meter had been tampered with.

Joan was devastated. She felt as if Agnes, supposedly her best friend, had knifed her in the back.

During the course of Agnes's hernia operation, she had a vivid out-of-body experience. She floated out from her own body which was lying inert on the operating table, right up to the ceiling of the operating theatre, from where she was able to look down, and could see the surgeon and staff at work on her abdomen. She flinched when she saw the incision and the vivid red blood and watched, fascinated as they were manipulating her intestines. She suddenly felt queasy and floated out into the corridor. All of a sudden, at the end of the long hospital corridor, she came across five or six figures, and at first they all looked hazy and out of focus.

Sounding concerned for Agnes's spirit, the figures shouted, "Agnes! Come here! Hurry up!"

Agnes drifted towards them – and could now make out three long-haired men and two women. They grabbed hold of Agnes and started to run down another long corridor, which became increasingly darker and colder, and as it did so, the faces of the people underwent a very unpleasant metamorphosis. Their features slipped and slid in a crazy way until they became grotesque, almost like gargoyles, Agnes remembered thinking. Their fingers were now transformed into claws which they flexed in and out, as they started to snarl and laugh, revealing long, pointed fangs. Agnes cringed as the monstrous devils shouted profanities and revolting phrases that she'd never heard before, and the entities warned her that she was entering the mouth of Hell. One of the women started to sink her fangs into Agnes's back. Then the others did the same. Agnes screamed with the pain as she experienced the sickening sensation of her flesh being bitten and torn away. She closed her eyes and started to pray, and the demons that had hold of her started to laugh, and cried, "Shut up! There is no god."

Agnes started to cry, and pleaded, "Save me, Jesus" over and over, and the demons started to scream at her.

All of a sudden, she felt a comforting, warm sensation, and a light shone at her from the depths of the darkness. In that light she saw the radiant face of an unknown bearded figure and then she saw a second face, and it was one she recognised from the days of her childhood. It was Mrs Blundell, her old Sunday School teacher. On seeing her, the demons suddenly scattered like startled rats into the impenetrable darkness.

When Agnes woke up she was back in her hospital bed on the ward. Sitting by her bedside was Joan. Agnes grabbed her hand and told her of the strange out-of-body experience. Then she confessed to all the bad things she had done in her life – things that shocked Joan – things that stretched back over years, including all the betrayals which Danny had uncovered on her computer.

Joan listened quietly to this shocking confession, and, being a compassionate type of person, and a loyal friend, she was able to forgive Agnes for all her bad deeds, even those involving herself, and now she and Agnes are the best of friends again.

For her part, Agnes now feels certain that Hell is a reality and that the Devil really does exist.

Unidentified Remains

In November 1987, thirty-one people died in the King's Cross Underground Station blaze. All of the victims were identified – except for one badly charred corpse. The male body remained anonymous, referred to only as 'One Hundred and Fifteen' by the coroner, and no relatives or friends of the unidentified victim came forward to put a name to the remains. It seemed probable that the body belonged to one of the many people in London who live rough and seek the warmth and shelter of the underground.

Over sixteen years elapsed until January 2004, when forensic experts from the British Transport Police finally concluded that 'One Hundred and Fifteen' had been a seventy-two-year-old man from Scotland by the name of Alexander Fallon.

After the death of his wife from ovarian cancer in 1974, Alexander Fallon had gone to pieces, eventually selling up his house in Falkirk and moving to London in the early 1980s, where he ended up living rough on the streets. At last, the mystery of Mr One Hundred and Fifteen had been solved.

Further back in time, another railway disaster created a similar mystery, but this puzzle has never been solved, though there are tantalising clues that may one day provide a solution.

It all began in the dark foggy hours of the Saturday morning of 13 October, 1928. At 4.28am, the Leeds to Bristol night mail steamed at a steady sixty miles per hour through dense fog and collided with a train that was being shunted on to a station siding. The mail train was thrown by the impact into the path of an oncoming freight train. In those days, railway carriages were gas-lit, and the cylinders of gas onboard the train exploded on impact, creating a raging inferno which tore through the carriages.

This nightmare scenario took place under the road bridge at Charfield Station, twenty miles south of Gloucester. A handful of locals who were out at that early predawn hour witnessed some amazing and terrifying sights. One sleeping passenger on the hellbound train had been awakened by the almighty crash, and had managed to stumble out of the door of his carriage, which was standing on its end. By pure luck, he stepped out from the train, directly on to the humped-back bridge above it, and he kept on walking, obviously in a state of shock, never to return.

Another man was wandering around in a daze, screaming out through the choking clouds and searing flames for the girl he was due to marry soon. All he was ever able to find of her was her handbag.

Some were lucky that morning, others weren't. The dreadful aroma of burning flesh, and the screams of the passengers trapped in their blazing carriages, horrified onlookers and would haunt the memories of the survivors for years to come. One rescuer broke down and cried when he heard the agonised pleas of a group of survivors pinned under a blazing carriage, begging for someone to cut off their legs, to free them from the blistering heat. Another man had to be punched unconscious because he refused to leave his trapped sister to die in the fire-gutted wreckage. She pleaded for help from him, and when he regained consciousness he could still hear her terrible screams.

What little remained of the Charfield disaster victims was very difficult to identify, and many relatives of those still missing accepted the railway company's offer to bury what was left of their loved ones in a mass grave in the village churchyard. Upon the memorial stone of that grave, ten names are inscribed, and at the bottom of the list are the words: 'Two Unknown'. The two unidentified bodies from the three-train pile-up had apparently been those of a boy of eleven or twelve, and a girl aged about nine, and, amazingly, no one had come forward to identify them. It is one thing for an old man to have no one in the world who cares about him, but quite another for two children to be burned to death and no one to miss them.

In the seventy-six years that have elapsed since the Charfield tragedy, the two forgotten children remain nameless and unclaimed. A porter on the doomed train named Haines distinctly remembered two schoolchildren being on the train at Gloucester station that fateful morning. Haines had moved along the train checking tickets, and had found the boy and girl travelling alone and overnight, a curious state of affairs, which fixed the sighting in the porter's memory. The children had their own tickets, and each had been wearing a school cap of some kind. Police Sergeant Crook later stated that part of a school blazer found among the crash debris, was of a size to fit a boy or girl aged between eight and ten, and had been an Air Force blue colour with black ribbon around the pockets. On the blazer was a distinctive badge with a floral design on a red background, and it bore the motto, 'Luce Magistra', which, when translated, means, 'By Light, Mistress'.

Despite these very specific clues and a nationwide publicity campaign via the national newspapers, no school in Britain came forward to claim the pupils, or to identify the badge and blazer. Neither did any parents or guardians come forward seeking their missing children, and therein lies the mystery of the forgotten railway children. Official and amateur detectives across the land tried to connect the blazer and badge with a school, but were unsuccessful, so it was assumed that the two mysterious children must have been educated abroad.

However, I researched this fascinating case many years ago and discovered that the Air Force blue blazer and it's Luce Magistra badge was worn – and still is worn – by the pupils of Queen Ethelburga's private boarding school near Harrogate. The ill-fated train on which the unknown children were travelling, was running from Leeds, which is very near to Queen Ethelburga's, yet neither the headmistress of the time, nor any of the school's teachers, contacted the authorities to identify the blazer and it's unique motto. This raises the possibility that the children were on the run from some kind of mental or physical abuse. But even if that was the case, how come they were never missed by their parents, friends and relatives? Perhaps they had uncovered some far-reaching scandal and had been fleeing to the safety of their parents' home by train. The possibilities are endless.

According to some of the Charfield locals, a mysterious woman in black was often seen visiting the grave of the two unknowns from 1929 to the 1950s. She used to step out of a chauffeur-driven limousine of German make, and then spend a long time staring at the memorial stone on the Charfield train crash victims' grave.

Does this have any bearing on the riddle of the forgotten railway children? And what has this intriguing story got to do with Liverpool hauntings? Well, on three separate occasions in October 1979, a Liverpool man named Tony O'Neil was visiting relatives in Cheltenham, and he certainly knew nothing about the Charfield train crash of 1928.

One evening, around 9.15pm, Mr O'Neil looked up from his newspaper, and was amazed to suddenly see a boy of about fourteen and a girl of around seven or eight years of age sitting on the opposite side of the carriage. The seats which the youngsters occupied had been vacant just seconds before. Mr O'Neil noted that the boy was wearing a dark blue school cap and uniform, and held a satchel on his knee. The girl was partly obscured by the boy, but she too wore a similar uniform. The boy turned towards Mr O'Neil with a sad expression on his face, then instantly vanished, along with the girl.

Tony O'Neil witnessed the appearance and dematerialisation of the same boy and girl on the train to Cheltenham at the very same time on two more occasions, and on 13 October – the anniversary of the Charfield crash of 1928 – the ghosts were not only seen by O'Neil but also by a woman passenger who let out a scream. Although the woman was shocked by the phantom schoolchildren, she noted that their reflections in the carriage window disappeared along with them too, as if they had been physically real. A railway ticket inspector at Cheltenham later told Mr O'Neil and the female passenger that the spectral schoolchildren had been seen on the train on many occasions.

Are the apparitions of the sorrowful-looking duo the earthbound spirits of Charfield's 'two unknown'? Perhaps they will continue to haunt the modern trains bound for Cheltenham until such time as we uncover their true identities and determine why they were travelling unsupervised on the train bound for nowhere.

Saved by a Bee

In *Haunted Liverpool 8* I introduced readers to an amateur Victorian sleuth, Mrs Gloria Hamlet, and her trusty side-kick, Florrie Perkins, who, between them, tackled many intriguing crimes. After being widowed at the age of twenty-nine, Mrs Hamlet left her Cheshire home and came to Liverpool, where she set up a small chandler's shop in Bold Street. Florrie helped in the shop, as well as delivering purchases to customers' homes on her bicycle.

Mrs Hamlet and Florrie Perkins obviously loved the challenge of solving local mysteries, amongst them the following bizarre tale.

One beautiful sunny evening in June 1881, at precisely 7pm, a thirty-one-year-old mathematics tutor, Lawrence Williams, was leaning out of the window of his top-floor lodgings, enjoying the view and smoking his pipe. As he puffed away, idly watching the people and carriages passing by below on Clarence Street – a huge bumble bee came buzzing through the air directly towards him. Williams batted the bee away with his pipe – and at precisely the same time, there was a loud bang in the street. A bullet whizzed past the maths teacher's head, grazing his cheek and shattering the mirror on his dresser. Williams dived for cover, and when his landlady Mrs Bronte came rushing into the room, Williams screamed at her to stay away from the window and dive for cover.

There were no more shots, and the police were soon on the scene. The bullet had been of a .44 calibre, and one detective thought the Fenians – an Irish terrorist group – could be behind the shooting. Only a week earlier the Irishmen had attempted to dynamite Liverpool Town Hall for their cause: home rule for Ireland. The houses on the other side of Clarence Street were searched, but no trace of any gunman was found, although they did uncover one possible lead, but the police didn't pursue it as thoroughly as they might have.

The window in a lodging house facing Williams's room had been left open, and the lodger – a Mr Sylvester – hadn't been seen since he left at eight o'clock that morning. His room was checked, and although a faint aroma of cordite hung in the air, no gun was found. The landlord said that Sylvester had paid a month's rent in advance. He had been a very, very small, quiet, inoffensive-looking man, yet other lodgers claimed that the gunshot had definitely originated in his room. Nothing seemed to add up, as Sylvester's room had been empty and locked at the time of the shooting, and no one was seen or heard to run from it. The landlord had rushed upstairs immediately after hearing the tremendous bang, and no one had passed him on his way up. If the gunshot had indeed come from that room, then the gunman must have been invisible.

Detectives then asked Williams if he knew of anyone who would want to harm him. The teacher thought long and hard, but couldn't think of anyone who might have a grudge against him. The strange incident was gradually forgotten, the police having decided that the whole thing had been an accidental shooting by someone messing about with a pistol, which did not warrant further investigation.

Mrs Gloria Hamlet, however, was not one to let a mystery rest and became fascinated by the incident. She not only interviewed Williams, but also visited the lodging house where the mysterious would-be assassin was thought to have had a room. The landlord took a liking to the attractive-looking detective, and upon her second visit to the lodging house he admitted – over a glass of sherry – that he had found two objects in the room which had been abandoned by the mysterious Mr Sylvester: a book of illustrated nursery rhymes, left open at a certain page, and a beautiful, expensive-looking clock. Mrs Hamlet inspected the clock, which was a French Japy Frères model, eighteen inches in height – not the sort of item a person would overlook, even if they were leaving in a hurry. The purple ribbon in the book of nursery rhymes had been left in the page that displayed the following verse:

There was a little man and he had a little gun,
And his bullets were made of lead, lead, lead;
He went to the brook, and shot a little duck,
Right through the middle of its head, head, head.

Perhaps the rhyme contained some kind of clue, Mrs Hamlet mused. She examined the clock, and noticed that the silver medallion on its front slid sideways. She then gazed through a hole in the back of the timepiece – and was shocked to discover that she was looking through a cross-haired gun-sight. The clock was carefully dismantled, and found to contain a .44 percussion revolver, with its trigger tied to a lever amongst the timepiece's cogs. The clock had been set up to fire the gun at 7pm – long after Mr Sylvester had left his lodgings for good.

The intended victim – Mr Williams – shuddered when he was told of Mrs Hamlet's findings, and he suddenly remembered the comical-looking 'midget' whom he and a friend had made fun of some three weeks before the shooting. They had belly-laughed at the diminutive man as he passed below the window. The teacher and his friend had been drinking and were quite tipsy that evening.

Williams was an idiosyncratic man of habit, and each evening, at precisely 7pm, he could be seen smoking his pipe at his window. The little man must have noticed this and, inwardly seething because of Williams's insensitive behaviour, had plotted his ingenious revenge. It could have been the perfect murder, had the bullet struck its target squarely. Instead, a humble bumble bee had saved the life of Lawrence Williams.

Mr Sylvester was never traced. He was undoubtedly a warped genius, and I have the unsettling feeling that he may have actually killed before, and after, the mysterious Clarence Street shooting. Perhaps his murders were executed so cleverly, that they were made to look like accidents.

An example of such a crime that comes to mind, was the discovery of a mysterious copper pipe that was found plumbed into the Corporation Baths in Archer Street, Kirkdale, in 1882. The pipe had been lethally linked to a lightning conductor with the undisguised intention of causing major harm. The pipe was quickly removed, and just who put it there remains a mystery. Had there been a lightning strike upon the conductor, many people in contact with water from the pipes would have been killed.

Ghostly Funeral Procession

In March 1979, a strange spectacle was witnessed by many people on the streets of Liverpool – a ghostly funeral procession from the Edwardian or Victorian eras.

At half-past noon, people having lunch in the window seats of Kirkland's Café on Hardman Street noticed a tall, gaunt-looking man in a long black coat, ambling slowly up the road outside. He wore a tall, silk, top hat with long black ribbons streaming from it in the cold March breeze. In his hand he held a staff with a black ribbon attached to it.

About twenty feet behind the old-fashioned jaywalking undertaker – or 'featherman' as they were called in times past – there followed two large ebony horses, their rippling muscles gleaming as they pulled an elegant four-wheeled hearse. Large, black, ostrich feather plumes bobbed from the harnesses on their heads. The coffin inside the elaborate, glass-sided hearse was barely visible because of the rose-wreaths and floral tributes which bedecked the carriage.

Three equally elaborate four-wheeled carriages formed the rest of the cortège, all horse-drawn, of course, presumably taking the mourners to the funeral service. The horses, carriages and featherman in his suit of mourning sable, all seemed real enough, and all the bystanders assumed that someone was merely being sent off in a particularly ostentatious style. Some said that the cortège had been spotted earlier on Rodney Street, and that when it moved off it proceeded through a red light, almost causing a fatal crash. The spectral hearse-driver continued to show a total disregard for traffic lights and other road users as he steered his horses across the junction into Myrtle Street. A Mini screeched to a halt, and the furious driver, showing a total lack of respect for the funeral procession, wound down his window to vent a mouthful of swear-words to the featherman and the hearse-driver. He even beeped his horn in a moment of pure thoughtlessness – but the horses of the cortège showed no response.

Later that day, the horse-drawn mourners were sighted going up Gorsey Lane, coming from the direction of the Ford Cemetery. Again, the cortège caused mayhem with the traffic, but when the police turned up in the area to take control of the situation, they could find no trace of the funeral procession. The featherman, the drivers and the bereaved alike, had seemingly vanished into thin air. The police made enquiries at the cemetery but no old-fashioned hearse and carriages had been seen in the vicinity that day, or any other for that matter.

It transpired that people in the neighbourhood of Ford Cemetery had seen the very same ghostly funeral procession years before in the 1950s, and some held the belief that the eerie vision preceded death and brought bad luck to those who beheld it.

Who Goes There?

I once read a yellowed, time-worn letter from a Mr R Gaskell of Stanhope Street, to Sir William Nott-Bower, Head Constable of Liverpool during the period 1881-1902. The letter was dated Saturday, 12 August 1899, and it related an intriguing story that blends crime and the supernatural. The contents of that letter, and further research of my own into its claims, have produced the following strange story.

In the Lancashire of the late nineteenth century, the name of a mysterious character in the underworld was tantalisingly heard time and time again, yet we know nothing about this person's background today, and the Victorian police were evidently none the wiser either. The name was Specolli and he seems to have been an elusive kingpin of crime in the days of Queen Victoria.

Specolli was rarely involved in crime directly, but seems to have had a league of lackeys and scoundrels at his disposal to carry out his ill-intentioned schemes. Specolli must have exercised a considerable power over his shady subjects in his dark realm of crime, as hardly any of them ever informed on him. Two that did were quickly silenced: one was found at the bottom of a dry dock with his head caved in, and the other was found hanged in the garret of his own home. His killing was made to look like suicide, with a note left at the scene of the hanging, even though the dead man was illiterate, unable to write even his own name.

Specolli's tentacles reached all four corners of the county, but especially Liverpool, where he was thought to be living, not far from the old Chinatown quarter.

In 1886, rumours began to circulate about the 'Aladdins Cave' of an eccentric old man named James Grundy of Cornwallis Street. All that was known – and is still known to this day – was that Grundy had a horde of gold, money, jewellery, works of art, bric-a-brac, and other valuable items in his cellar, which was cordoned off from the coal cellar by a partition wall of granite. He had reams of inventory papers that listed the items of treasure, and those papers came into the hands of Mr Gaskell who first alerted me to this peculiar case.

The wealthy, but mentally unhealthy, Grundy, would prowl the alleyways at night, delving into dustbins and picking through midden heaps for scraps of food. Occasionally he would even resort to begging to sustain himself, anything rather than dipping into his fortune. Despite his attempts to keep his fortune secret, somehow, somebody found out about it, and the whispers and rumours rippled across Liverpool and eventually reached the ears of Mr Specolli.

Specolli's first reaction was to try and put the rival criminals of the region off the scent by spreading a rumour about a quantity of gold bullion being temporarily stored in a dock warehouse in the north of Liverpool. Specolli even sent a bogus tip-off letter to a major criminal in the form of a business proposal. Under the name Williams, he stated that he had been unfairly sacked by a certain bank and now wished to exact his revenge on his former employees by providing inside information on the security procedures at the warehouse, in return for reasonable remuneration.

As the rival crooks of the city were occupied with the bogus proposal, Specolli sent his spies out to Cornwallis Street to watch over Grundy's house, and they gleefully noted that the old man had not even taken the precaution of adding secure locks to his doors, or bars to his windows. The spies reported back to Specolli, and he mentally drew up the plan to steal the treasure from the cellar strong-room.

Specolli's supreme lock-picker, a man named Crilly, and a brute nicknamed 'Tubby' Rogers, would enter the premises with Grundy at night when the rich old eccentric had returned from his scavenging. They would then force him to open the vault, after which Tubby would keep him downstairs and bind and gag him. Crilly would go to the drawing room window of the house and give a signal to a third accomplice, and he in turn would light his pipe, to signal to the four-wheeled 'growler' coach waiting on the corner, in the shadows of St Michael's graveyard. That coach would call at Grundy's home and transport the valuables to a half-way house on Harrowby Street, three quarters of a mile away. The loot would be divided and taken to five separate locations, to be left there until the heat died down.

This is where the story takes a turn into the uncanny. Specolli's carefully thought-out plan went smoothly and James Grundy was parted from his long-hoarded treasure. For safety, the booty was hidden in different locations, and one fifth of it was sent to the cellar of a house in Anfield. In the seclusion of the cellar the haul was examined, and amongst it there was a small wooden chest, about two feet in height and five feet in length. It was secured by several large padlocks. Upon the lid of the chest, a small silver crucifix was stapled with strips of green-tinted copper. In faded chalk, the three words 'from the *Amity*' had been scrawled on the side of the chest.

The thieves were naturally impatient to discover what was contained in the securely-bound chest, but not having the expert lock-picker Mr Crilly at hand, they decided to use hammers and chisels instead. When the lid was prised off that chest, an icy draft blew out of its interior, and the sound of laughter echoed throughout the cellar. Specolli's two lackeys were thrown about by an immensely powerful force. As soon as they had regained their footing, they ran out of the cellar, and as they dashed to the front door, the sound of heavy running footsteps pursued them. For several streets the invisible pursuer kept up the chase, until the eerie footsteps faded away. Crilly and Rogers were so terrified by the supernatural incident, that they refused to return to the cellar until daybreak.

By the time the thieves conjured up enough courage to go back to the house, the loot had been stolen, probably by some chancer who had wandered into the house after seeing the front door standing ajar.

The police investigated the robbery at James Grundy's house and a few minor arrests were subsequently made, but, as usual, Specolli – the mastermind behind the whole thing – escaped, and the other four fifths of the loot from Grundy's cellar was never recovered.

Decades later, it was rumoured that Specolli had given himself a new identity and gone to live on the Isle of Man to escape several violent members of his own family, who were thought to be recent Italian immigrants. Specolli was said to be easily recognisable to the police because he had a prominent black mark under his left eye – apparently the scar left by an adder bite sustained in childhood. Despite this, Specolli vanished into obscurity.

The intriguing part of the tale concerning Grundy is the sinister wooden chest from the *Amity* stored in his cellar with a crucifix stapled to it. The sailing ship the *Amity* was built at New York in 1816 and she served the Black Ball Line of sailing packets between New York and Liverpool until 1824, when she was wrecked on Squam Beach, New Jersey. The *Amity* was one hundred and six feet and six inches in length, with a beam of twenty-eight feet and a hold over fourteen feet deep. She once made a crossing between Liverpool and New York in just twenty-two days, yet this fast and reliable ship had acquired quite a sinister reputation. It was claimed that she was harbouring something supernatural that few superstitious Jack Tars in New York or Liverpool were prepared to even talk about, for fear of incurring forces that cannot yet be comprehended by mortals.

In the 1820s these weird rumours about the *Amity* were seemingly confirmed when the ship arrived at Liverpool Docks from Rexton, New Brunswick, after a voyage of twenty-eight days. Beneath the casks which made up most of the cargo, in the floor of the hold, the body of a partially decomposed man was discovered. His off-white eyes bulged obscenely out of their sockets and his emaciated face, though discoloured and shrunken, still wore an expression of raw terror. It seemed as if he had died from fright, as the coroner was unable to determine the cause of death. Rumours were rife and swept through the Liverpool docks like an ill wind. Some said the body was that of a deserter who had hidden in the *Amity's* hold, but enquiries by the Canadian police at Brunswick disproved this, and the corpse was never identified.

Crew from the *Amity*, most of them unaware of the grisly discovery in the hold, gathered in the waterfront taverns of Liverpool and whispered about the nerve-wracking 'thing' that haunted their ship during its recent voyage. It had all started some months back when the *Amity* was locked in ice in the Canadian harbour of Richibucto. The cold that winter was so severe, that a crewman lost his nose to frostbite, and ship hands risked losing their fingers as they handled the ship's rigging which was permanently coated with a thick layer of snow and ice. As temperatures continued to plummet, the captain and crew were forced to take temporary refuge inside the stricken ship, where they huddled together supping extra tots of rum and whiskey to ward off the intense cold. Even down in the cabins they could still see their breath and could not sleep because of the cold.

At three in the morning, the officer of the watch blew furiously on his frozen fingers and stamped his feet in an effort to keep out the cold and was counting the minutes to the end of his watch, when he heard the sound of someone, or something, treading on the creaking sheet ice, which had the ship in its vice-like grip. He looked over the rail and saw nothing but a low sea mist suspended in a layer across the frozen waters. He spat overboard nervously and the saliva instantly turned into crystals, stinging his already chapped lips.

Later that morning, the crew not only heard the sounds of someone walking through the ship's hold, they also claimed to be startled by the pale misty exhalations of breath from something that was invisible to their eyes.

The ghostly entity then made itself scarce for a week, but when the *Amity* finally broke free from the ice, 'the Invisible' as the First Mate called the phantom, suddenly became very active once again. The captain tried to calm the nerves of his terrified crew by claiming, rather lamely, that the ghost was nothing more than the sounds of the ship's timbers settling back into place after their long exposure to the sub-zero temperatures. All the same, the captain slept with a lamp at his bedside and with the ship's Bible within easy reach. The Invisible allegedly materialised from time to time during the voyage to Liverpool, and when it did so, the sight was so shocking, that one old sailor almost died from heart failure. The descriptions of the entity varied from "a fiend that looked like Old Nick himself" to "a slimy, lizard-skinned devil".

Whatever the thing on board the *Amity* was, it seems to have departed the ship at Liverpool Docks, for the ship's crew never experienced another paranormal incident after that voyage was completed. The identity of the dead man found in the *Amity's* hold was never determined, and so we must assume that he was a stowaway, who had perhaps died from starvation, dehydration or hypothermia. Or perhaps the 'thing' literally scared him to death.

All of this makes me wonder if some skilled occultist or exorcist managed to contain the ghostlike being from the *Amity* and imprison it in the locked chest with the crucifix attached to it. How and why James Grundy had come into possession of the chest is another mystery. If Specolli's cronies unwittingly released the invisible creature, what became of it? Scarier still, could it still be at large?

Gremlins, Goblins and Little Green Men

The time was around 8pm on the humid evening of 1 August 1966, and fifteen-year-old David Ashton was kindly washing the dishes for his grandmother in the kitchen of her home on Empress Road, Kensington. There was a huge full moon that night, and David watched it through the upper pane of the kitchen window. He switched on the Decca transistor radio on the window ledge and a song called *Little By Little* sung by Dusty Springfield came blaring out of the speaker.

At that moment, David was shocked to see two tiny silhouettes pass by window. In that fleeting moment, the teenager saw that they were the shadowy figures of two miniature people, about eight inches tall, walking along the top of the back yard wall. David put down the bottle of washing-up liquid and peered through the window, then he felt his stomach somersault with fright, because the two little figures were now standing on the wall, facing him, with the full moon shining behind them – and they seemed to be watching him.

David had never used a swear word in front of his grandmother in his life, but that night he was so terrified by what he was seeing, that he shouted a profanity and dropped a plate into the sink before running out of the kitchen. "Nan!" he yelled, and his grandmother looked up, startled, from the book she had been enjoying. David told her what he had just seen and he urged her to come into the kitchen to see for herself. His grandmother, Margaret, could tell by the serious expression on her grandson's face that he had seen something which had deeply perturbed him, so she went into the kitchen with him, while listening to his far-fetched claim. However, when she looked through the window, all she could see was the glowing orb of the summer moon.

Moments later, the furious barks of every dog, in every back yard along Empress Road, simultaneously erupted outside. Margaret unlocked the door and she and David stepped into the back yard, listening to the canine cacophony. All of a sudden, Margaret witnessed a sight that made her think she must be dreaming. Two small figures, that looked like small dolls, came sprinting along the top of the yard wall, and as they passed Margaret and David, the beams of light shining out through the kitchen window panes caught the little sprinters, momentarily showing them to be of a greenish colour.

David impulsively felt the urge to take his grandmother's electric torch (which was reserved for emergencies) and go into the alleyway to chase the little green men, but Margaret forbade him. She pushed him back into the kitchen, then locked and bolted the door. The old woman felt there was something evil in the night air outside, and she drew the kitchen curtains, then shuddered as she thought about the undersized green men. She remembered all the childhood tales her Clitheroe mother had told her about the 'boggarts' – mischievous, grotesque-looking goblins who brought bad luck to those who sighted them.

It seems that other people saw the green goblins that same month. I have reports of strange green lights seen moving about in a hedge in Fairfield and Newsham Park, and a classic description of a gnome-like being that was seen prowling about after dark in the vicinity of St Mary's Church and the gardens of nearby North View, Paddington.

Strangely enough, two years before, the *Liverpool Echo* had reported several outbreaks of 'fairy mania' in various parts of Liverpool and beyond. For example, in 1964, huge crowds gathered near the bowling greens off Kensington's Jubilee Drive, when children reported seeing little gnome-like men in white hats throwing stones and tiny clods of earth at one another. Several people later came forward and claimed that the entire thing was a hoax, perpetrated by children dressed up in white woollen hats and colourful jumpers, but many people, including trained observers such as policemen, asserted that the strange little beings that put in an appearance on the bowling greens were not human by any stretch of the imagination.

*

I have in my files, many letters from readers who claim to have had encounters with what could be termed little green men. I have received quite a few accounts of the 'Kirkby Goblins' which were seen in the mid-1980s. One reader told me that when she was three years of age, she often wandered down to a pool in her aunt's garden in the Southdene area of Kirkby. Her aunt warned her to stay away from the pool in case she fell in and drowned. The child forgot about the warnings one day and was kneeling by the pool, when all of a sudden, a little green figure wearing a cone-shaped hat popped out of the water and warned her to stay away. The girl screamed and ran to her aunt and told her about the green man in the pond, but she assumed the girl had been merely startled by a frog.

This 'little girl' was in her late teens by the time she wrote to me about the incident, and she swears it wasn't a frog that saved her from a possible tragedy in that pond – it was an elf!

I have heard an almost identical account of a helpful elf in the Knowsley area. A twelve-year-old schoolgirl going down a lane in Knowsley in the early 1980s was said to have seen a little green-coloured man jump out of a hedge. The impish being said, "Do not go down the lane," then vanished. The girl turned on her heels in fright and hurried to school by an alternative route. The girl later learned that a man had been attempting to entice children into his car in the lane where the imp gave his warning.

Here is a letter from a reader named Gillian concerning little green men that could only be seen by her son.

Something strange happened in a house I lived in during the 1970s. My son was about four years old at the time. My husband was working the night shift at Vauxhalls and as I felt a bit nervous sleeping alone, I used to take my son into bed with me.

This particular night I was lying there, telling him a story, expecting him to doze off, as he usually did. He kept sitting up, and became very unsettled. I asked him what the matter was, and he said he was watching the "little green men" flying around the room. He told me that one was sitting on the small cupboard in the corner. I saw nothing and didn't give his tale any credence. This went on for some time until he threw himself under the covers and started to cry. Through the sobs he said that he didn't like "the big one standing at the bottom of the bed". At this point, I also felt a bit scared, and followed him under the covers!

The next morning I told my husband. He was pretty annoyed I had taken Robbie in bed with me again and said it was my own fault. In the light of day it all seemed pretty stupid and I had a little laugh at myself.

That was the end of that, until a while later – and I can't recall if it was weeks or months – when a neighbour who lived next door but one laughingly told us a tale about his wife waking the household in the middle of the night screaming hysterically about little green men running and flying around the room. The woman's husband and daughter thought it was hilarious at the time and advised her to see a psychiatrist as they thought she was, "going batty with the menopause"! My husband and I sat there dumbstruck, staring at

*them. For our neighbour's wife it was a great relief for her to know she wasn't going mad.
I was absolutely horrified.*

*My son and neighbour never saw the green men again. Soon after that we moved to
Canada and lost touch with the neighbours.*

From little green men, boggarts and goblins, we move now to another genus in the family of the leprechauns – the gremlin. Gremlins are traditionally a very grotesque form of imp that used to be able to cause havoc with a farmer's plough and horses, as well as causing major problems with the most basic agricultural machinery in the era before the Industrial Revolution.

Today, people talk of 'gremlins in the system' when electronic devices such as computers malfunction for no apparent reason. This is an unconscious throwback reference to the gremlins that could freeze a horse with an evil stare and cause a plough blade to break. The name 'gremlin' is not as old as the creature it describes, and many who are interested in folklore may not be aware that the name was invented as recently as the early twentieth century. In the 1920s, during RAF operations in India and the Middle East, pilots had a predilection for drinking a beer named after its brewers – Fremlin. Some have claimed that when airborne pilots reported an inexplicable malfunctioning in their planes, the sceptics would say that the 'Fremlins' were to blame – meaning the pilots were drunk! 'Fremlins' was misheard, or slurred, to become 'gremlins', or so the story goes. The author Roald Dahl has even claimed that it was he who invented the name while he was in the Royal Air Force.

The etymology is beside the point; in earlier times, a gremlin would have been called a 'cluricaune' – a gruesome-looking elf with evil tendencies and a malevolent psychical influence.

Stretching back many years, at least to the Edwardian period, there have been lots of curious sightings of a creature that fits the description and behavioural patterns of a gremlin, on Liverpool's Dock Road.

*

In 1919, four soldiers who had just left the *Aquitania* at Liverpool's South Docks, reported seeing an ugly-looking, two-legged creature with dark grey fur, a large pair of red eyes and two large pointed ears. It was chased as far as the Salthouse Dock, where it quickly vanished, seemingly into thin air. During the pursuit, one soldier fired a pistol at the 'animal' and it not only made a squealing sound, but it shrieked out what sounded like the word 'bastard' in a parrot-like tone. An old Irish stevedore told the soldiers and several other witnesses that the creature was an old troll and warned that the soldier who had fired upon it would be severely cursed for the next seven years.

Our Norse ancestors respected the troll both in Britain and their native Norway. According to Norse folklore, trolls are solitary, big-nosed creatures that hunt alone and have a vicious, violent streak. They are prone to melancholia and have a brown or grey coat of fur interspersed with prickles that stick out protectively when the troll is in danger. In past centuries there are dozens of reports of lone wayfarers crossing remote tracts of Lancashire, Cheshire and Yorkshire being attacked by trolls and left for dead.

One such victim – a young pit boy from Yorkshire – staggered into an inn one evening, moaning and bleeding profusely from deep claw marks on his stomach and legs. The traumatised lad's clothes were in tatters, and when he managed to stammer out his story, he claimed that he had been set upon by a troll. The boy told how he had accidentally startled the troll as it was feasting on the carcass of a hare, and it had chased him and attacked him.

*

The winter of 1962-63 was the severest one the country had experienced since 1740. Anticyclones to the north and east of the British Isles brought bitter sub-zero winds from the east day after day, and Liverpool, like many other major cities in the country, was almost brought to a standstill by phenomenal snowdrifts.

In January 1963, a Martindale coal merchant's lorry was labouring through a blizzard down the black-iced Dock Road, when the vehicle hit a small animal, crushing it under its front left wheel. The wagon slithered to a halt seconds later on the almost deserted road, and when one of the coalmen looked out from the passenger window, he saw a weird-looking creature stumbling away on two legs. It was about two feet in height and was saturated with blood. The unidentified bipedal creature clambered over a snowdrift and then seemed to tumble into the Salthouse Dock. The lorry's driver also saw the bizarre creature, but the cold was so intense, that he and the coalmen had no intention of leaving the relative warmth of their cab to investigate its fate.

The previous story was related to me by a former coalman, and the following story, which took place in the same area of the city, was told to me by the two people in the tale, who were children at the time of the incident.

*

In the summer of 1975, Gary and Ian, two fourteen-year-olds from Toxteth, were playing truant and were messing about in the derelict warehouses of the Albert Dock. This was in the days before the docklands in that area were renovated during the massive regeneration schemes of the 1980s. The two lads were smoking a cigarette in turns as they strolled along the derelict colonnades, close to where the Tate Gallery is now located, when they both spotted something on one of the paving flags, next to one of the huge pillars. As the boys approached what looked like the rotting corpse of a cat, a thick swarm of bluebottles flew off it. Gary had a fascination for the macabre and the gruesome, and as he stooped over the decomposed body, he saw that it had two short arms with pink, claw-like hands and two legs with tiny, human-looking feet – quite unlike a cat. The body was covered in grey fur, and the head was round and positioned face down. Ian held his hand to his mouth as the putrid aroma of decay assaulted his nostrils.

"What is it?" said Gary, placing his shoe on the head of the corpse and squashing down slightly. "Er! Look at its eyes!"

Two red cylindrical eyes, like two over-ripe plums, popped out from each side of the head with the pressure.

"Aw! Leave it alone. It stinks!" said Ian, still holding his nose. "You're making me feel sick."

He turned away from the rotting lump of flesh and, as he did so, he spotted something that froze his blood on that hot summer's day. Standing out of the glare of the sunshine, in the cool shadows of a warehouse doorway, was a little old man, about two feet in height. His body was also covered in grey fur, except for his face, hands and feet, and he had a small pot belly. His face looked wizened and creased, and his nose was globular and oversized. The eyes were just shadowy sockets. Ian was so petrified by the sight of the furry old man, that he didn't even stop to warn Gary; he simply ran off at top speed.

Moments later, Gary was running close behind him. The boys were so spooked by the weird encounter that they didn't even dare to look back to see if the unsightly little being was in pursuit.

No one ever believed Ian and Gary's story, and the boys never ventured near the Albert Dock again.

*

Early in 2002, I heard yet another account of the Dock Road gremlins, and this time it came from two women who spotted a strange creature on Strand Street. The time was around 9.30pm, and the women had been working late. They were walking through a car park to their car when they saw what looked like a tiny old man ambling towards them down Strand Street. Gradually, as the odd-looking figure drew nearer, the women could see by the light of a sodium lamppost that he had a big, bulbous nose, and a face full of menace.

One of the women couldn't help yelping with fright – which startled the strange little man, who hadn't noticed them up to that moment. He gazed at the two women with an angry frown, then came running towards them. The women threw themselves into the car, and within seconds, had reversed the vehicle out of the car park, away from the peculiar entity that had been chasing after them. When the driver gazed in her rear view mirror, she could see the shadowy little figure creeping back into the darkness.

What are we to make of all these sightings and encounters with trolls, gremlins and little green men? It has been suggested that the Dock Road gremlin is nothing more than an over-large sewer rat. This mundane explanation came from an old former policeman who had had a waterfront beat many years ago. He said that he had once come across an elderly sewer rat with a grizzled old face that resembled that of a miserable old man. The rodent stood on its hind legs as it licked its paws and groomed itself. In a certain subdued light, the rat could have been perceived as some sinister two-legged creature not unlike a troll.

That's one possible explanation, yet somehow I think the truth is probably much more complex. I have always had the suspicion that some mystery mind manipulator has been influencing our minds throughout history. I visualise the Manipulator as some timeless higher intelligence from somewhere else that creates ersatz versions of the Virgin Mary, UFOs, goblins and certain ghosts, just to see how we react. This invisible watcher may gauge our reactions just as a behavioural scientist watches a rat negotiating a maze.

Of course, all the legends from long ago state that, once upon a time, there were ancient races of supernatural beings that included fairies, trolls and their ilk. These diminutive peoples dwelt mostly in what is now Western Europe, and they were concentrated in the West of Ireland, the Isle of Man, the outer isles of Caledonia, Wales, Cornwall, Cumbria and Lancashire. The Celts were the only humans in Britain who lived in harmony with the fairies and trolls, but the warring races that invaded the isles afterwards drove most of the little people underground into warrens, caves and mounds.

The next assault on the fairy folk came from the Christians when St Augustine came in the sixth century with his cross, to banish demons and the 'faeries of old'. The few people in rural areas who held the last human contact with the little people were threatened by the Church to break all ties with them. All the same, at the closing of the day, families would gather at the inglenook and the grandparents would recount enchanting fireside tales of the little folk and their ways, and that is how the stories of the fairies were passed from generation to generation.

Today, many people are disillusioned with traditional religions, and are beginning to look back to the planet-loving ways of the Wicca. If world peace ever becomes a reality, and human beings ever stop abusing the planet and 'get back to the garden', the fairies and trolls may one day come out of hiding.

That's a big if!

Death Was a Stranger

One of the most curious stories I have looked into began one morning on a certain Liverpool street in the summer of 1997. A thin gangly man, aged about thirty, with long greasy hair, a faded blue tee shirt, stained jeans and grimy scuffed tennis shoes, came slowly down the street. His stubbled face was turned down to the pavement and he seemed to be so engrossed in his own sad thoughts that he was unaware of anything else around him. Tracking him at a walking pace, came a black BMW, cruising down the street a few yards behind him. In the car were three shaven-headed men, all in their twenties, and all wearing expensive, brand new track suits and immaculate, costly trainers.

The windows were wound down and the skinheads surveyed the scruffily-dressed pedestrian with unpleasant smirks on their overly-tanned faces. The driver, in his designer shades, glanced back and forth between the street and the scruffy man.

Minutes later, the BMW rolled to a halt outside the large house where the three skinheads lived and worked. Their occupations lay in the criminal sphere. They committed burglaries on a regular basis and supplemented their income, whenever it was necessary, by distributing a variety of drugs to the neighbourhood junkies. However, in recent months, the trio had been forced to suspend their drug-pushing activities because a determined team of narcotics officers had been repeatedly raiding suspect premises in the area.

We'll call the three shaven-headed n'er-do-wells Lee, Paul and Jason – not their real names.

The three of them sprang out of the BMW and jokingly seized the dishevelled man and jostled him towards the house. He meekly protested as two of the skinheads manhandled him down the hallway, through the back-kitchen, and out into the sunny back yard. The eldest of the criminals, Lee, went upstairs and returned shortly afterwards brandishing a pair of electric hair clippers, with no comb attachment fitted.

Jason and Paul roughly removed the stranger's clothes and when he pulled away and raised his voice in protest, they slapped his face and told him to shut up. Every item of clothing, including his dirty underwear, was removed from 'the hippy', as they now decided to call him, and Jason proceeded to shave off the poor man's hair with the clippers. The transformation from dishevelled, grubby, oily-haired beatnik into a streamlined hygienic skinhead was almost complete. The man was bundled into an almost unbearably hot shower and scrubbed by six hands. Afterwards, the stranger was shaved, and Hugo Boss cologne was slapped into his face, which was speckled with shaving cuts. The former drop-out was treated to some Calvin Klein underwear and a smart tracksuit from Wade Smith.

The newly groomed guest was thankful but had severe doubts about their motives and was quite anxious to leave the house, but Lee, Jason and Paul told him to relax and sat him at a table where one of them laid a thin line of coke.

"What's your name, mate?" Lee asked, putting his arm around the unknown man.

"John," came the reply.

"Well, John, have some whiz."

Lee pushed John's face down towards the line of white powder.

"No, I'm sorry, but I'm not into drugs," John mumbled, apologetically.

"Are you a retard?" Jason asked, seriously. He thought John's apparent slowness of mind and clumsy actions belied some kind of mental problem.

Lee's temper flared. He was a very muscular man and he grabbed John's arm and yanked it up his back, then pushed his face into the coke powder. John groaned – then puffed and blew away the powder, which resulted in him receiving a beating from all three. He was bundled into a spare room in the house and kept there under lock and key. John tried to shout for help but his captors would blast music as loud as they could from a CD player to blot out the noise. The neighbours were so afraid of the drug dealers, that they never complained to them, or the police.

Three days later, John was still being held captive at the house, when he was escorted downstairs to a back room where Lee, Paul and Jason were smoking marijuana. It was eleven o'clock in the evening and the vertical blinds were open, admitting silver stripes of moonlight from a full summer moon. A radio was whispering on low volume, and a crimson lava lamp undulated hypnotically on the mantelpiece.

John was pushed into a deep leather armchair, while Lee sprawled out on a sofa, and talked about feeling tranquil, and Paul and Jason sat on the floor, gazing up at a tank of tropical fish on the sideboard. John refused to smoke any pot, but Lee was so drugged, that this time he took no offence and accepted his captive's refusal. As the night wore on, the skinheads lost all sense of time, and the drug seemed to remove the false personas of the street-hard tough-guys.

"Wonder if a swan can break your arm, just by flapping its wing," Lee suddenly mused, and started to giggle, thinking about the way his father would warn him not to go near the swans on Sefton Park's boating lake when he was a boy.

"Wonder why the moon's round and not square," Paul idly remarked, watching the moon sinking ever so slowly beyond the silhouetted rooftops.

Jason exhaled a perfect smoke ring from his rolled-up joint and murmured, "Round is natural."

All the external doors were locked, and so John was allowed to make himself a cup of tea in the kitchen. The effects of the drug and the mellowness of the summer evening were conducive to an unexpected mystical discussion about life after death among the criminals.

"I reckon there's something after this, deffo," Jason said, staring at the luminescent graphic equaliser display on the radio.

"Yeah, a six foot hole," was Lee's response.

"Yeah, but say you get cremated?" Paul asked.

"Okay, then, there's just an urnful of ashes. A mixture of other people's ashes mixed in as well probably."

"What d'you mean?" Jason asked.

"I heard that they save a few bob by cremating a few bodies at once," Lee told him with a smirk.

"That's well out of order," Jason protested.

The subject turned to ghost stories, and each of the skinheads told a supernatural tale, then they asked John if he knew any ghost stories.

John shook his head, then added, "But lot of strange things have happened to me though."

"What like?" Lee said, suddenly propping himself up on one arm and taking an interest. He rested on his stomach, then focused his attention on the abducted 'guest'.

"People around me always die," said John, flatly.

At that moment, Lee, Paul and Jason felt a sudden cold current of air from the open window brush against the back of their necks.

"How d'you mean, 'always die'?" asked Lee.

"I've lost my entire family to accidents, to cancer, to suicides. I've had five girlfriends in my life and they've all died within months of my meeting them. I'm like the angel of death. Like a fatal jinx on everybody I meet."

"Maybe you're just unlucky," Jason said, after a long tense pause.

"No, it's more than that," John replied, "I'm like the Grim Reaper, and I don't know why. When I was young I was put in one school after another. Teachers died: in fires, car crashes … Friends I made choked on sweets, were murdered, or knocked down … The schools would change, but the outcome was always the same. It's gone on and on and I'm so tired of it. Behind me there's a trail of dead bodies."

"No way!" Lee said, and, he saw how nervous Jason and Paul seemed all of a sudden.

That night, when John was put back in his room, the skinheads argued amongst themselves.

"I'll let him go in a few days. I'm just hanging on to him for a laugh," Lee explained to his younger accomplices.

"There's something not right about him, Lee," Jason said. "He gives me the creeps."

"Just let him go now," Paul suggested. "What's the point of keeping him?"

"You big soft tart," said Lee. "In a few days we'll let him go. He's just a weirdo. Now get to bed."

On the following morning, Jason was soaping himself in the shower, when he felt a hard, round lump under his armpit. It was not at all painful, but it was very definitely a lump, and he panicked.

He told his mates about it as they ate their cornflakes, trying not to sound as if he was scared. Paul advised him to go to the doctor's straight away, but Lee dismissed the lump, saying it was probably just an overactive sweat gland.

Later that day, there was a frantic knocking at the door. It was Lee's mother, and she was in floods of tears. Her brother – Lee's Uncle David – had just died. Lee's dad had died when he was a child and his Uncle David had raised him like a father. Lee's mother said she had found her brother hanging out of his bed, clutching his chest and gasping for breath. He had asked her to get an ambulance, but he died from what looked like a heart attack before she could even get to the telephone.

During the confusion, as Lee rushed to his mother's home, John slipped out of the house, back into the obscurity of the street.

Within a week, Paul was dead from an accidental heroin overdose. His blue bloated body had lain decomposing in the shared house while Lee stayed a week with his grief-stricken mother. When he found Paul's corpse, it was covered in maggots and bluebottles.

Jason did go to the doctors with his lump and was quickly diagnosed with cancer. He was sent to Clatterbridge Hospital to undergo a programme of intense chemotherapy.

A month later, Lee's mother was deserted by her lover of six years, and that, coupled with the traumatic loss of her brother, caused her to suffer a nervous breakdown which resulted in her needing treatment in a psychiatric hospital.

From Clatterbridge, Jason wrote to me about these tragic incidents, and the claims of the mysterious John. Jason was convinced that John was some kind of harbinger of death, and sadly, months after writing the letter, he lost his battle against cancer.

In 1999, Lee committed suicide by attaching a pipe to his car exhaust and feeding it into his BMW in a garage at a house in Brighton. At the time of his death, there were rumours that he had recently been diagnosed with AIDs.

Was the spate of deaths nothing more than a cluster of dark coincidences? Or did the weird stranger actually cast a shadow of death on his captors?

Spooked Crooks

In the eighth volume of *Haunted Liverpool* I included a chapter about police constables and their encounters with the supernatural, entitled, 'Tales of the Blue Lamp'. In this chapter I'd like to narrate the personal accounts of criminals who have had encounters with the paranormal and the downright uncanny. Not all of these skirmishes with the inexplicable took place during the hours of darkness.

One gloomy Wednesday afternoon in September, 1968, Mick, a twenty-one-year-old small-time thief and pickpocket from the Dingle, was at the Pier Head. He was apparently just enjoying the panorama and fresh air, but was actually scanning the passers-by to find a likely target. Suddenly, a woman of about seventy, with a tight mop of white hair, came walking past Mick. She had her purse wide open, and it looked healthily packed to Mick's practised eye.

The young crook tailed the woman inconspicuously, and as she walked along, he watched her slip the purse into the right pocket of her long mackintosh. Mick pursued the woman until she stopped at the long rail that ran along the promenade adjacent to the floating landing stage. The pensioner surveyed the rise and full of the buoyant landing stage, the dark choppy waters of the river, and the ferry chugging across to Birkenhead, then, after a while, she walked off to the buses lined up nearby. The woman boarded the bus that went to the south of Liverpool via Renshaw Street – the street where Mick the pickpocket was about to get a nasty shock.

As the green bus left the Pier Head, the woman settled down next to a window on the lower deck – and Mick positioned himself directly behind her. They were the only two passengers on that deck. Two youths who boarded the bus went straight upstairs. Mick wondered if he could reach down and put his hand through the small gap at the back of the bus seat and carefully extract the purse using his light-fingered skills. He also considered waiting until the woman had left her seat, later in the journey, to get off at her stop. Should he use this tried and tested method which had worked for him many times before, in which he would pretend to stumble against her as the bus came to a halt and take the opportunity to dip his hand in and out of her coat pocket to whisk the purse away.

As Mick pondered on the method he would use to steal the old woman's money, he gazed at the back of her head in front of him, and among her curls of ivory white hair, he saw something move slowly, and it made his heart jump. He leaned forward slightly, and to his utter horror, he saw a pair of dark, bloodshot eyes peering out at him from the back of the woman's head, blinking slowly. Mick recoiled in horror from the glistening eyes, and before he could get to his feet, the old woman spun round and let out an asthmatic chuckle.

"I've been watching you, love. I know your game!"

Mick sprang up out of the seat, horrified, and then noticed that the woman held a small knife in her hand. Mick rushed to the front of the bus and frantically asked the driver to stop. Reluctantly, the bus driver let Mick off at the next set of traffic lights. He didn't dare look back.

The woman with eyes in the back of her head was responsible for giving Mick many nightmares for years to come. He never saw the woman again, but later heard that a woman with an extra set of eyes had once lived near Lark Lane. She often tied a scarf around her head to cover up her deformity, as the children in her neighbourhood used to laugh and make fun of her. I assume that when this woman died, her unusual four-eyed head would not have gone unnoticed by the coroner.

People with four eyes usually cannot see with their extra pair, but there is a case on record of a man with rudimentary occipital eyes that would follow a moving light source.

*

Another unusual incident that was related to me by a member of the criminal fraternity, took place one stormy night in 1977 in the leafy suburb of Aigburth.

A burglar called Eddie shinned up the drainpipe of a house in Alexandra Road and quietly eased up a window frame. Within moments, he was inside the house, which he knew to be deserted after casing the residence for quite some time. Once safely inside the luxurious house, Eddie turned on a small flashlight which had a piece of red cellophane taped over its glass to project a subdued light.

He crept stealthily up the stairs, with the torch casting distorted rosy shadows of the banister and its rails along the walls. The time was midnight, and being in an unfamiliar old empty Victorian house at that hour would give most people the creeps, but it was all part and parcel of Eddie's 'job', and he was not in the least bit worried. His mundane thoughts were focused solely on the quantity of jewellery he believed to be stored in the upstairs master bedroom.

Eddie was about five steps from the landing leading to the bedroom full of loot, when a high-pitched scream pierced the air and shattered his nerves. A little girl of about five years of age, dressed in an old-fashioned white nightgown, came rushing along the balcony. She looked terrified, and she turned right at the end of the landing and started to come down the stairs. Her tiny bare feet padded down the carpeted steps, and Eddie froze.

The girl brushed past the burglar, out of breath, with tears in her eyes. Her coal-black hair was tied into pigtails, and they bobbed and swung about as she rushed down the stairs, repeatedly looking back with an expression of pure terror on her face. Then came the sound of a man's voice, growling and shouting a string of unintelligible words. The voice sounded as if it was coming from the master bedroom, and it was getting louder all the time.

Eddie rushed into a room off the landing, and had begun to close the door slowly and gingerly behind him, but before it closed, he felt thumps vibrating through his feet from the floor, as someone heavy came pounding down the landing. A huge, hairy, naked man with an enormous pot-belly passed the partially opened door, and Eddie shrank back; the last thing he wanted was a confrontation with this over-sized brute. It had not escaped his notice that the man was brandishing a brass poker, and from the bottom of the stairs came the horrifying screams of the little girl.

Things were not going according to plan – Eddie had found himself in the wrong place at the wrong time, and felt certain that the naked man was about to murder the child. He wracked his brains and wrestled with his conscience; something which he had not done for a long time. Should he get involved, or should he abandon the theft and quickly slip out of the house and telephone the police?

Eddie left the room, crossed the landing, and saw something that chilled him to the bone. He could see the shadows of the man and the girl moving on the wall. The shadow play made Eddie numb with fright. The man was bringing the poker down repeatedly on the little girl's body, and the sickening thuds sounded identical to the noise of a golf club swiping up turf. After about four or five strikes, the agonised screams stopped abruptly, and there was total silence.

The overweight man then made his reappearance at the bottom of the stairs, still brandishing the bloodstained poker. He lumbered back up the stairs, puffing and panting and cursing under his breath. Eddie was gripped with a feeling of intense fear and loathing for the murderous brute, that throbbed painfully in the pit of his stomach. He dashed into the smaller bedroom, and struggled to raise the sash window. Being old, the sash was difficult to open and beads of sweat broke out on his forehead as he grappled with it and the murderer's footsteps grew ever closer.

The sash eventually gave way and Eddie scrambled out on to the narrow window ledge and tried desperately to reach for a drainpipe, but it was just beyond his reach. He stood balancing on the ledge, and as he did so, Eddie heard the bedroom door burst open, followed by the sound of the murderer's voice. He jumped towards the slippery, cast iron drainpipe, but failed to grip it properly, and slid forty feet down it, badly scraping his legs and hands.

When Eddie's feet hit the ground, the impact winded him. He collapsed on to his back, and discovered that he could not breathe in properly. He crawled away down the drive, and somehow managed to scramble to his feet, halfway down the street. Once he had regained the power to breathe again, he ran to a public telephone box and called the police to alert them to the child murder at the house he'd tried to burgle.

Eddie scanned the *Liverpool Echo* on the following day and watched the local news programmes on television, but there was no mention of any child being murdered in Aigburth.

Many years later, Eddie was drinking in the Jolly Miller pub in West Derby one night, and he and his friends were talking about the subject of the supernatural. In the course of the conversation, a woman mentioned that she had a cousin who lived at a house on Alexandra Drive that was haunted by the ghosts of a little girl and a naked man who chased her down the stairs. Eddie's blood ran cold, because he had told no one about his terrifying and inexplicable ordeal during the aborted burglary at the Aigburth house. He listened intently to the woman, who said that the two ghosts had been seen regularly since the 1940s, and they always went through the same actions, as if some terrible murder from long ago was being re-enacted.

*

There was once a dilapidated mansion that stood in the suburbs of Blackpool, which had a reputation for being haunted by a very unusual entity – a silver sphere, the size of a billiard ball. What strikes me as remarkable, is the number of crooks and opportunist scrap metal salvagers who have written and emailed me with tales concerning the crumbling house.

In the 1970s, two Liverpool men descended on the mansion as twilight was falling. The intruders immediately noticed that the fireplace surrounds in the house were in pristine condition, and would definitely fetch a pretty penny if sold to the right buyer. The men set about removing the first surround – when a small silver globe, about three inches in diameter – floated out from the fireplace, appearing to have emerged from the chimney. The pair from Liverpool ran out of the room as if their lives depended on it and jumped straight into their van outside. They never returned to the mansion again.

What they didn't know was that other people who had entered the house had been confronted by the same hovering metallic sphere. A tramp had sought refuge from the rain in that same mansion a year before, and he had awakened to find the silvery orb circling round him. The vagrant sensed something evil in the chrome 'bubble' and so he threw a chunk of fallen masonry at it and fled.

One theory that was put forward to explain the phenomenon was that a magician who used the floating silver spheres trick as part of his repertoire, had once lived – and died – at the old derelict mansion, and that he was still performing tricks from beyond the grave, but no one knows the true origin of the silvery orb.

The Cannibal

The following story is the full version of a tale that was only mentioned in a brief paragraph in *Haunted Liverpool 1*.

I uncovered this gruesome spine-tingler in an article which I found in the nineteenth century newspaper, the *Liverpool Albion* and a short version of the story has appeared in one of my earlier books, but here is the grisly story in full.

In July 1884, a cargo-carrying brigantine called the *Pierrot* set sail from Montevideo for a return journey back to the port of Liverpool. The *Pierrot* was a large vessel, some one hundred and ten feet long and thirty feet across the beam. She weighed two hundred and eighty-two tons.

The ship was under the command of a seasoned old Liverpool captain, Edward Grace, a man who was renowned in the city's maritime community as a sinister eccentric. Grace was known to be a member of a bizarre club in London known as the Society for the Acclimatisation of Animals in the United Kingdom. This was an organisation devoted to increasing the nation's food supplies by breeding any exotic creatures, from kangaroos to bison, in the fields of England.

The founder of this fellowship of crackpots was a friend of Captain Grace, Francis Buckland, a wealthy surgeon and eminent naturalist. Buckland was notorious for eating such dubious delicacies as boiled elephant trunk, mice on toast, and stewed mole garnished with blue bottles. On one occasion, Buckland and Grace allegedly even ate the preserved relic of a French monarch, Louis XIV, which had been plundered from the royal tomb during the French Revolution. Buckland and Grace did not even suffer from the slightest trace of indigestion after this repellant feast, and both agreed that the heart had tasted much better when eaten with gravy made from the blood of a marmoset monkey.

Only two members of the *Pierrot's* crew of nine knew about their captain's perverted appetite. They were First Mate, Jack Burbage and Second Mate, Albert Cribbin, who both found Grace to be a repulsive and domineering man. They had vowed never to serve under his command again after the Montevideo voyage was completed.

However, in the middle of the Atlantic, the *Pierrot* ran into a violent storm, which blew the vessel into an uncharted rock. The rock created a thirty-foot gash in the brigantine's hull, and the ship's hold rapidly started to fill with water.

As if this state of affairs were not dire enough, an enormous wave then swamped the stricken vessel and swept five crewmen over board. Captain Grace and the four surviving crew members managed to launch the life boat and proceeded to row away as rapidly as they could from the rapidly sinking ship, before the suction could drag them all down with it.

As the survivors rowed furiously, they heard a desperate voice shouting to them. The old cook stopped rowing and pointed to a head, bobbing up and down next to the lifeboat. "It's the purser, Mr King!" he cried.

Captain Grace uttered a stream of profanities then said, "He's damned! Leave him. Save yourselves."

"We can't just leave him to die, sir," pleaded the sixteen-year-old cabin boy, Richard Tomlin, who had also stopped rowing.

The other two rowers in the boat, the First and Second Mates, were also regarding the drowning purser sympathetically.

Knowing he was risking the Captain's wrath, the old cook let go of his oar and, leaning over the side of the boat, reached out towards the purser saying.

"Quick," shouted the furious Captain Grace. "He'll capsize us! Let him be."

The cook took no heed of Grace's warning, so the Captain picked up the elderly man's oar and lifted it high above him. The three other survivors watched, speechless with shock, as Grace brought down the oar on the cook's head and smashed his skull like an eggshell. The sickening impact sent blood spraying out of his ears and the old man toppled overboard into the sea. The abandoned purser swore at the Captain and grabbed hold of the corpse in a vain attempt to stay afloat. Grace then turned to the other survivors, still wielding the oar in a threatening manner.

"Row this boat from here right now, or you'll follow him!" he warned in a grim low voice.

The trembling cabin boy Tomlin, and the two other men, did as he said, and by some miracle, the boat survived the storm.

Then the real hardship began. The lifeboat drifted aimlessly upon the vast expanses of the Atlantic Ocean, under a bleaching, blistering sun all day, and through the freezing, biting cold of the night. The survivors soon became thirsty, but they had no water to quench their parched, dust-dry throats. They tried gargling with the salt water, which only made them vomit, and stung their blistered lips. The Captain and his surviving crew were soon suffering from heatstroke, dehydration and starvation.

Day after day they scanned the distant horizon for ships, or what would have been an even more welcome sight, the coastline, but they saw nothing other than bobbing waves for as far as their tired eyes could see.

By the fifth day, the survivors were too weak to row for more than a few minutes at a stretch, and it seemed to be only a matter of time before they died, one by one, of thirst and starvation.

But the ever-resourceful Captain Grace had a suggestion – a suggestion so horrible that it immediately sent shivers down the spines of the two officers and the cabin boy. The Captain coughed to clear his dried up throat and in a gruff, parched voice, he announced, "There's only one alternative left to us. We draw lots, and the unlucky one gets eaten."

The First Mate flinched in horrified disbelief and shook his head vigorously.

Undeterred, Captain Grace opened the lifeboat's small medicine box. All it contained was a roll of bandage, a small phial of iodine, and a needle and thread. He suggested cutting four lengths of bandage. The one who chose the shortest length would be killed to feed the other three.

"No, Captain! Someone will pick us up soon, " argued the Second Mate. "It can't be long now. A ship's bound to pass us soon."

Grace ignored him and took out his clasp knife. "It's the only way we can survive. We eat animals, don't we? Well, a man is just an animal too. They do it in the Polynesian Islands."

"It's three against one, sir," said the First Mate, picking up the oar, ready to hit the Captain with it if necessary.

Grace smiled, then put the knife back in its sheath and said, "You're right. I can see I'm outnumbered." And he closed his eyes and pretended to doze off.

In the golden rays of the following morning's sunshine, the First and Second Mate awoke from a fitful night's sleep to a nightmare. The Captain's mouth was dripping with blood and with a sickening feeling they realised that he was in the process of eating the cabin boy, Richard Tomlin. He had evidently slit the poor lad's throat during the night, probably while he was sleeping, and was now carving the flesh from his forearm with the clasp knife. The ravenous villain made vile slurping noises, and seemed unaware that he was being watched by the other two. Fearing that he might be next, the First Mate, Jack Burbage, picked up the heavy oar and struck the cannibalistic Captain across the head with it. The blow sent Grace reeling across the boat, and he came to rest on his back, out cold.

The two officers stared in horror and disgust at the remains of slaughtered teenager, then Burbage picked up the captain's clasp knife and knelt down, ready to slit Grace's throat. The Second Mate persuaded his colleague not to commit murder, or it would look as if he had killed the cabin boy as well.

When Grace regained consciousness, he saw the First Mate standing over him with the knife.

"I ... I only did it so we could survive," he stammered, seeing the murderous look on Burbage's face. "I ... I didn't want to kill the boy."

Over the next two days, the First and Second Mate had to take turns to sleep, because they obviously couldn't trust the demented Captain Grace and they didn't want to end up like poor Tomlin.

But through the combined effects of starvation and thirst, the officers became so weak that, in the end, they both collapsed, leaving them at the mercy of the Captain. Surprisingly, Grace didn't harm them; instead, he attempted to nurse them back to health by force feeding them with the cabin boy's flesh. To stop the skinned corpse from perishing in the noonday heat, he had dipped a roll of bandage from the medicine box in the seawater, then wrapped it around Tomlin's body.

Several days later, when all three men were close to death, a British naval vessel sighted their boat and came to the rescue. The sailors from the ship felt nauseous when they realised that the grotesque bundle lying in the bottom of the boat was actually the bandaged corpse of a boy; a corpse that was no longer intact. And when the sailors saw the streaks and smears of blood around the mouths of all three semi-conscious survivors, they soon put two and two together.

Captain Grace and his officers were taken to Portsmouth and charged with murder, but the Home Secretary thought the men had been through enough already, so he commuted their sentences to six months' hard labour at Dartmoor prison. When Grace had served his time, he changed his name and grew a beard before returning to Liverpool to look for work. He soon found employment as a stevedore, but the moment he was paid at the end of each week, he would squander his entire wages in the saloons of the Dock Road.

It was around this time that the hallucinations began. One night he saw the decomposing face of the cabin boy he had murdered, peering at him through the window of a pub called the Crow's Nest. On another occasion, as Grace was staggering drunkenly down Paradise Street in a swirling fog, he was confronted with the bandaged and bloodstained corpse of Richard Tomlin. The cabin boy, almost devoid of any skin and flesh, held his arms out to the terrified ex-captain and chased after him.

These grotesque and distressing hallucinations became steadily worse, and wherever Edward Grace ventured out in the city, the thing in bandages followed him. In the end, Grace ran into a police station in a frantic state and ranted on about the awful revenge which Tomlin's ghost was exacting on him. Smelling the alcohol on his breath, the police surmised that the only spirits troubling the hysterical old man were those of the alcoholic kind, and they decided it would be in the public interest to throw him into a cell for the night.

Accordingly, Grace was locked up in the Anfield Road Bridewell to sleep off the drink, but on the following morning, he was found dead in his cell by the officer on duty. The mariner's body was discovered lying curled up under the iron bed, and his eyes were wide open with a look of sheer terror. In Edward Grace's right hand, he was clutching a bloody strip of torn bandage …

The Giant Spectre

The following story, concerning the world of crime meeting the world of ghosts, is briefly referred to in an old Edwardian book called *Knaves and Crooks*, by Dudley Dunning, and takes place between Liverpool and London.

Close to Garlands, the flamboyant, hedonistic nightclub on Eberle Street, just a stone's throw away from Dale Street, and just a stone's throw back in time, there was once a Turkish Baths where many hard-worked Victorian gentlemen used to escape from the pressures of mental and physical toil in the elaborate marble pools, pore-cleansing steam clouds, piping hot water jets and cool drinking fountains.

Within this relaxing marble sanctuary of sweltering vapours, one rainy March afternoon in 1886, two sophisticated burglars were whispering ideas to each other for possible 'jobs' they had their sights on. John Lee Yates and William Pryde, both aged fifty-two, discussed attractive opportunities in their sphere of crime. Mr Pryde described his ingenious plans to remove priceless silverware from Knowsley Hall, and Mr Yates countered it with in-depth talk about a magpie's nest of jewellery and gold which, he had been reliably informed, was ripe for the taking at Gawthorpe Hall, the stately home of the Shuttleworths.

However, their entreprenurial chit-chat was soon cut short by the speedy approach of the stout bath attendant. The flabby fellow handed Mr Pryde a sealed envelope with one hand, while wiping away the sweat which was permanently erupting on his forehead, with the other. He informed Mr Pryde that the letter had been given to him by a small round man in a pea-green suit outside the baths and that he had pressed it upon him in a most urgent manner. The description was immediately recognisable as 'Dicey' Devine, a small-time fence who often worked for Yates and Pryde.

Pryde tore open the envelope and read Dicey's distinctive handwriting, riddled, as usual, with appalling spelling mistakes. As he did so, an expression of shock passed across his flushed face.

"Fingerspin is out," Pryde said, and handed the note to Yates.

Within minutes, Pryde and Yates were dried and dressed and were speeding in a hansom cab to their luxurious lodgings on Botanic Road in Edge Hill, next to the park. They scurried up to their rooms, and there was Henry Player – expert lock-picker, pickpocket and cracksman extraordinaire, nicknamed 'Fingerspin' by his colleagues in the underworld.

He slouched back on the chaise longue lighting a Guinea Gold cigarette with a match, seemingly oblivious to the recent entry of Messrs Pryde and Yates.

The burglars bolted straight into the 'loot room' where their chests of swag were kept under lock and key, fully aware that the heavy padlocks on those chests would not have hindered Fingerspin in the least, should he have decided to take a look inside. He had been picking those types of locks, often in the pitch dark, since he was a kid. With great relief though, Pryde and Yates soon discovered that the chests were still full of booty. Their pickings and ill-gotten gains were intact.

"I suppose it would be obtuse of me to ask how you gained access to this private apartment, Mr Player?" asked Yates, haughtily.

"Why, I let myself in, Mr Yates," was Fingerspin's offhand reply.

He rose from the chaise longue and silently circled round the shop window mannequin which was wearing a topper and a salt and pepper overcoat, which stood improbably in the corner. Pryde had been using the dummy to teach himself pickpocketing skills, without much success. Fingerspin nonchalantly brushed against the mannequin, and moments later, he presented the dummy's empty wallet to Yates and Pryde, as if he were displaying a winning poker hand.

"What do you want with us?" Pryde asked, nervously re-checking the stash of silver in the chest.

Henry Player sat down again and told them he had just completed a five-year jail sentence for house-breaking. Now he was free, but, unfortunately, stony broke. Managers of the shop, Lewis & Co, of Ranelagh Street – later destined to establish the famous Lewis's store – had been supplying free breakfasts to the unemployed for a month, and Henry had been very grateful for that morning meal, but now he wanted to live the high life once again, which would naturally necessitate resorting to a life of crime.

Henry Fingerspin Player then told his attentive listeners that those five long years in the cold Liverpool prison had been spent in the company of an old cockney named Nathan Yelski, who had been serving a ten-year sentence for defrauding a London bank. Yelski had been slowly dying from a consumptive disease, and Henry had looked after him well in the cell they shared. Yelski came to look upon Henry as a son, and Henry looked up to the old Hebrew as a fatherly figure.

Yelski's knowledge of locks was encyclopaedic, and he was also well acquainted with every loophole in English law. He would have made a first-class barrister, in fact, but had misused his brains and turned to crime instead. On many occasions, Yelski even managed to pick the lock of the cell-door, but he and Henry would never dare to venture out on to the prison landing for fear of harsh punishment and a sentence increase, and so the door would be locked again before the warders came along on their regular rounds.

Yelski was also gifted in the art of hypnosis, and the warders avoided looking him straight in the eye because of his mesmerising powers of suggestion. Weeks before the old man died, he revealed a marvellous secret to Henry, concerning the Bank of England. The secret was communicated to Yelski by an insider who had worked at the bank for many years.

Pryde and Yates sat on chairs opposite the released jailbird, hanging on to his every word, and carefully considering them with every swirl and winding ectoplasmic exhalation of Guinea Gold smoke. Fingerspin said that in 1836, the Directors of the Bank of England received an anonymous letter from someone who claimed to have access to their gold bullion store. The writer of the letter said that he could prove this by meeting them in the bullion vault at a pre-arranged hour. The directors concluded that the letter was the work of a hoaxer initially, but the staff at the bank took the letter's claims very seriously. The directors announced to the Press that they would wait in the bullion room on a certain night, and they actually went through with it. They assembled in the vault and waited with lanterns and pistols at the ready.

Sure enough, a scratching sound was heard in the bullion room that night, and the directors waited tensely for the cheeky bank robber to show himself. Presently, two floorboards on the cellar floor parted, and a head popped up. The head belonged to a man in his forties, although he was not a robber, but a sewerman. He'd been working in a sewer that ran under the celebrated bank, when he had noticed several bricks missing at the top of a drainage tunnel. The sewerman had then discovered, to his amazement, that directly above this tunnel was the bullion room of the Bank of England. On his first visit he had pushed the floorboards away and found himself among crate after crate of gold bars. The sewerman had refrained from committing any crime, and for his honesty, he was rewarded by the bank with a gift of eight hundred pounds.

However, that sewerman had a big mouth, and when he had been drinking a little too much Gold Watch in the local taverns, he would reveal, to anyone prepared to listen, the real reason behind his apparent honesty towards the 'Old Lady of Thread Needle Street'. He was terrified of the giant shadowy ghost that had attacked him when he made his first attempt to steal a box of gold bars. In most people, fear of the supernatural is greater than the desire for money, and this was certainly so in the case of the sewerman. He had scrambled from that bank and slipped head-first down into the murky stagnant waters of the sewer when the phantasm made a grab at him. Its fingers were long and grey – and icy, and they had grabbed at his neck as he was hanging the lantern over one of the bullion boxes. The thing had been at least seven feet in height, and its skeletal face was twisted with evil hatred as the sewerman reflexively held the lamp up to get a better look at it.

The old sewer worker had considered returning with a few of his friends for back-up, but that would have meant a share-out, and worse still, a mad gold rush to the vaults if they told their families. Then would surely come the risk of penal servitude. No, the shrewd sewerman decided that fake-honesty was the best policy, and so he had written anonymously to the bank authorities, offering to show them the vulnerable weak spot in their bullion room. As far as he was concerned, the more bankers who turned up in the vaults, the better, because the sewerman had no wish to meet that ghost on his own again.

Well, the bankers duly turned up and the sewerman rendezvoused with them, and thankfully no ghost materialised. He was well rewarded, but the money was gradually whittled away over the years, until the subterranean sanitation worker decided to take another look under the bank, and this time he went armed with a Bible and a silver crucifix, and was accompanied by his strong but slow-witted son.

On this occasion another branch of the sewer was discovered. This one was much smaller, and in a dangerous state of subsidence, and ran straight under the floor of the bullion room. The sewerman made a chaotic attempt at removing one of the bricks from the arched ceiling of the sewer, and almost caused a cave-in. He retreated, fearing three things: being buried alive under a collapsed sewer, arousing the unwanted attentions of the ghost, and being heard by the people in the bank.

The sewer worker and his son therefore retreated, trudging their way through the dark labyrinth of brick-vaulted passages that spread for forty miles under the metropolis. The sewerman drew up a crude map of the sewage tunnel system beneath the Bank of England, and would often unfold it on the counter of the local tavern, before boring the drinkers and barflys with his daring schemes to enter the bullion rooms. All hot air of course, but one day, a young Nathan Yelski happened to see those plans, and bought them from the sewerman – with a forged banknote. Yelski later acquired the uniform of a sewerman – a blue smock, waterproof boots, and the slouch hat – then set off to survey the dangerous sewer.

In the dead of night, Yelski carefully prised open a manhole cover in a quiet street in the Old Jewry area of London, and gingerly ventured underground carrying a lantern. After quickly ascertaining that the sewer under the bank was in a perilously decrepit state, he turned around and went back the way he had come – all the time with a cold suspicion that he was being watched. Yelski was a secular materialist, with no interest in the world of spirits and superstition, but he had an overpowering feeling that the eyes of something were upon him when he was in the vicinity of the bank.

Yelski returned to his lodgings in the East End to mull over the situation. He decided that he would need specialised equipment and an accomplice to carry out the job, and in the meantime, he resorted to several frauds to keep the wolf from the door. For one of these frauds Yelski was arrested, tried and imprisoned, and during his incarceration, he shared a cell with a man named Sperry, who had worked as a cashier at the Bank of England – until he was caught selling quantities of the bank's special banknote paper to a group of forgers. Sperry told him that there was a reinforced safe in the bullion room of the Bank of England that contained the most priceless diamonds in the world.

One particular diamond in the safe which had remained in Sperry's memory, was the forty-four carat stone, the size of a large quail's egg, with two-hundred and six facets. It was a grade D, and of a flawless briolette cut. It was perfectly clear, and even when magnified twenty times, no fissures or imperfections were detectable. Because of the diamond's purity and uniqueness, it was valued at around £3 million. It was called the Paragon Diamond.

Sperry shocked Yelski when he said that he knew the combination to the diamond safe, but he would take the secret to the grave with him. Yelski promised that he would pay Sperry dearly for the secret of the combination once he was released in a year's time. Sperry belly-laughed at the offer.

Almost a week later, Yelski waited for the right moment, when he and Sperry were sitting on the bottom bunk in the cell, enjoying a brief game of cards before the lights went out. He gazed right into his cellmate's eyes and told him he looked fatigued. Sperry was soon caught by Yelski's hypnotic stare, and within minutes he was under the mesmeric spell. Within the short span of those minutes spent in a trance, Sperry revealed that the combination to the diamond safe was not a number at all. The safe was not unlocked by a single wheel, but by five small brass thumbwheels, each with letters on, and the letters that opened the safe spelt the word 'Simon' – the name of the Chief Cashier's cat.

Sperry gradually came out of the trance without realising that he had been hypnotised, thinking he'd been merely dozing, and unaware that he had revealed the most closely guarded secret of his life.

"Well, to cut a long story short," said Fingerspin, "Just before Nathan Yelski died from consumption, he revealed the password to me and described the plan of the sewer under the Bank of England."

"That's a tall story if I ever heard one, Finger," sneered Pryde.

"Why are you telling us all of this?" Yates asked.

"I think we can pull it off between us, and then live like princes," Fingerspin said. "I can think of no two better accomplices."

"Rob the Old Lady? That's well out of our depth," gasped Pryde, "Jail's turned your mind."

Nevertheless, weeks later, at four in the morning, the three Liverpudlians blundered through a thick shroud of London fog, then stealthily descended into the stygian depths of the sewer system via a heavy, cast-iron manhole in the Old Jewery area of the capital. With each step, great brown sewer rats scampered away, as the three men slipped and slithered along the foul underground alleyways. They soon located the right sewer, and Pryde was immediately able to see the dangers at first-hand. He said it would be madness to risk a cave-in by removing bricks from the unsafe sewer to reach the bullion room – the whole lot could come down on top of them. Fingerspin carried a small pick and as he held the lantern up to inspect the loose, moss-covered bricks, he urged Pryde to reconsider, as they were all so near to an unimaginable fortune.

"It's suicide, Finger," Yates told him, "If that lot comes crashing down on us we'd be crushed before we had a chance to run. We need a supporting frame; a derrick ..."

"Think of that diamond ..." said Fingerspin, temptingly, "... the Paragon."

"We'd never reach it, Finger; not without specialist equipment. It's just too risky."

At that moment, Pryde turned, and saw something that left him cold. On the walkway on the other side of the rushing channel of effluent – an abnormally tall black figure loomed, and it was watching them. It seemed to be about seven feet in height. Yates saw the giant silhouette too, and he and Pryde turned simultaneously to tell Fingerspin about the eerie watcher – when tragedy struck. Fingerspin, determined to get at the treasure, had levered loose a couple of bricks from the arched ceiling of the decaying sewer – and the bricks and clay they supported collapsed on top of him. The shadowy tall figure emitted a terrifying moaning sound and leapt straight across the channel and on to the walkway. Without a thought for Fingerspin, Pryde and Yates fought one another as they scurried away. Each looked back just once, and saw the sinister goliath hunched over the half-buried body of Henry Player.

When the two Liverpool cracksmen surfaced in the Old Jewry, they gasped and trembled in the foggy night air, then ran off through the ghostly vapours. They did not dare to go back to see if Fingerspin was dead or alive, for fear of being spotted by the police – and most importantly, for fear of encountering the inhuman thing that had appeared down there in subterranean London.

For years afterwards, John Lee Yates and William Pryde scanned the newspapers to see if the remains of Fingerspin had been discovered. Surely a sewerman would have come across the body? Or had the rats eaten the remains of their partner in crime? Not a word was ever published in the press to satisfy their grim curiosity.

However, on 2 August 1933, in a bizarre twist to the story, excavations were being carried out under the Bank of England, when a lead coffin, measuring seven feet and six inches in length was uncovered, at a depth of almost nine feet. The giant coffin bore a metal plate with the inscription: 'Mr William Daniel Jenkins. Died 24 March 1798, aged 31.' The skeletal body in the coffin measured six feet seven and a half inches – very tall by today's standards, but a veritable giant in those days. London historians soon carried out research, and it was discovered that the body was that of a Daniel Jenkins who had once been a clerk at the Bank of England. So the mysterious ghost in the sewers was probably his.

Some months before his death in 1798, Jenkins had undergone a dramatic change of character which had led some to think he had been possessed. He would scream and sob, and was convinced that he was about to die. He also confided to his family that he had a morbid fear that his body would be dissected by curious surgeons and put on display because of his abnormal height. The Bank of England arranged for Jenkins to be treated by its own doctors, and when their clerk passed away from a heart attack, the directors of the bank arranged for him to be buried in the bank garden!

In 1923 an Act of Parliament had provided that any human remains interred in the bank's garden court should be re-interred in Nunhead, near Peckham, and so that is where the mortal remains of the giant William Jenkins now rest.

There is an interesting footnote to this story. William Pryde stole a number of expensive diamonds in 1889. Detectives placed his Botanic Road flat under surveillance, and Pryde was observed leaving the apartment one morning and then strolling into the nearby park. A whistle was blown, and several policemen ran into the park and arrested Pryde inside the Botanic Gardens. Pryde was searched but he did not have the stolen gemstones on his person. He had obviously known that he was being watched. He is said to have dug a walking cane into an area of soft soil and put the diamonds down the hole, before covering it over with his foot.

As far as I know, those diamonds, which were valued at £20,000 in 1889, were never found.

Escape into Yesterday

A personal mystery has haunted me for a couple of years, and this is the first time I have ever written about it. I had a friend in the 1990s named Robert who had an avid interest in history. In 2002 he vanished without a trace, and has never been seen or heard from since. A good friend named John was a closer friend to Robert, and he has always maintained that this disappearance was supernatural. I'll explain why.

Robert believed that he had been born a century too late. He had a love of the Victorian period, and despised life today. He found modern living to be devoid of any class, romance or adventure. He would laugh scornfully at grown men wearing garish shell-suits and white trainers, likening them to over-grown toddlers in one-piece romper suits and white baby shoes. According to Robert, the thumping digital music churned out in the twenty-first century was repetitive, stale and pre-programmed by computers, and the so-called singers were also artificially manufactured. Talented composers and musicians and innovations in pure, raw, analogue music had apparently ceased to exist. Television programmes fared no better, in Robert's opinion. People who were hooked into watching mindless reality shows would waste the time of their own petty lives to gawp for hours at celebrities asleep in their beds in mock-up houses located in sound-proofed television studios.

Robert saw life in the twenty-first century as some digital dystopian nightmare – somewhere between Huxley's *Brave New World* and Orwell's *Nineteen-Eighty Four*. The tasteless, additive-laden food was inferior, genetically modified and synthetic. Sugar didn't taste as sweet any more, and beer, brewed in aluminium and plastic containers, no longer got you drunk the way it once did. Robert desperately wanted to escape from today's world. He wanted to voyage back in time to the rip-roaring world of adventure and meaningful 'real' life in the Victorian era. Everybody has nostalgic hankerings for the seemingly happier times of yesteryear – the good old days – but for Robert, the nineteenth century was his real home, the only place he could be happy.

He knew I was very interested in time travel, and often wrote to me, asking if I could somehow transport him back to the 1880s, as if I had a time machine ready at my disposal! I did, however, tell him about one line of research which I had undertaken in the area of time travel; the power of the mind to move along the fourth dimension of time. I told him how I had experienced psychological time-displacement on several occasions that might have been induced by meditation. The mind has no mass or dimension, and so it could in theory be pushed along the time continuum, but our consciousness seems firmly stuck in the present, held there by our own habits of constant concern about our mundane everyday life in the present.

In *Haunted Liverpool 8*, I have mentioned one of my experiences of limited time travel into the past. I also believe that time travel will one day be accomplished through electronic hardware, but it is still a little way off yet.

Rob readily took up on my theory of psychological time travel and agreed that the mind was capable of many things we hadn't even dreamt of. He asked me for advice on what books to read and what practical exercises he should carry out to achieve it. I recommended that he should read all he could about a mystical freethinker named Gurdjieff, who believed that we are all trapped in a type of self-centred sleep, and that those who attained a truly 'awakened state' would become sufficiently enlightened to be able to shake themselves out of their everyday somnolence.

I also suggested that Rob should study hypnosis – an effective tool for focusing the mind sharply, and I told him how I had once witnessed an intriguing experiment in hypnotic time travel in the late 1980s.

In 1988, a seventy-five-year-old man named Geoff was dying of lung cancer in the Royal Liverpool teaching hospital. His ward was situated on the ninth floor of the eleven-storey building, which gave him quite a panoramic hi-rise view of Liverpool, with the grand sweep of the Mersey behind the cathedrals winding its way up to Runcorn with its distinctive suspension bridge. To the right-hand side of this vista were the misty mountainous peaks of North Wales, and way down below, Geoff could see people who looked like so many ants walking up and down Pembroke Place, West Derby and Crown Streets. With the exception of the old Prince William pub and the former Royal Infirmary Hospital, most of the buildings were modern, and belonged to the sprawling campus of Liverpool University.

Days before Geoff passed away, his friend Ben, a qualified hynotherapist, visited him. Ben was forty-five, and had known Geoff for about a decade as a neighbour. On the sunny afternoon of Ben's visit, he and Geoff were gazing out of the ninth floor window, discussing how things had changed in the city over the years.

"Trams used to go along there," said Geoff, pointing to the road below. "They turned up from Crown Street and into Pembroke Place."

Ben then turned around and checked that most of the patients in the small ward were either asleep from the effects of medication and illness, listening to the hospital radio, or reading. A nurse left the room, and Ben turned to Geoff and whispered, "Geoff, would you like to see Liverpool the way it was when you were a boy?"

"How do you mean?" asked Geoff, with a puzzled look.

"Would you like to see the trams travelling down Crown Street again?" asked Ben, in his normal polite, softly-spoken voice.

Geoff chuckled gently, and nodded, "Oh! You bet I would!"

Ben told Geoff to close his eyes, then he placed his thumb and forefinger very lightly over the terminally ill man's eyelids. He then told Geoff that when he opened his eyes he would find himself at the age of ten, looking down on the Liverpool of his childhood.

"Now… !" he said.

Ben gently lifted his thumb and finger off his friend's eyelids and Geoff stared down. He called out in panic and lifted his arms in a reflex action – because he could no longer see the ward he was in. He had opened his eyes to find himself floating above the streets of Liverpool at the dizzying height of the hospital's ninth floor. Ben gently held Geoff's arms and reassured him that he could not fall. He asked him what year it was, and the old man told him that it was 1923. He then asked if he knew what the actual date was, and Geoff stated that it was Friday 15 June 1923. This seemed odd, because the real date was actually Wednesday 15 June 1988. Ben wondered if 15 June 1923 had actually been a Friday. He later consulted an almanac at the city library in William Brown Street – and discovered that, in 1923, the fifteenth day of June had indeed fallen on a Friday. In certain states of consciousness, the human mind can perform abstruse calculations, and Ben bore that possibility in mind. Perhaps Geoff had merely calculated the day and date. Using mental arithmetic, many people can tell you the day of the week on which you were born, just by knowing your date of birth.

Then Geoff cried out excitedly, "Look! The trams are running down there!"

He named their numbers and their colours and described the way the sunlight glinted off their polished bodywork. He was also able to give a running commentary on the street life in the most accurate detail. This hypnotic view of 1923 had to be swiftly brought to a close when a doctor approached with a nurse. They had come to check on Geoff.

Two days later, Geoff passed away, smiling contentedly as he reminisced about old Liverpool and the people and places he had loved and missed so much.

Well to return to Rob – the man who wanted to emigrate back to the reign of Queen Victoria – he became fascinated by this account of hypnotic time travel. He read book after book about auto-suggestion and hypnosis, and painted the walls and ceiling of a room in his home black, which was somewhat over-drastic. He would sit cross-legged for hours, repeating mantras in his mind in an effort to transport his consciousness, if not his physical body, back in time to another era.

One night Rob telephoned John in a state of some excitement and said he'd made something of a breakthrough. He had heard the clip clop of horses in the street outside. John dismissed the sounds as having been nothing more unusual than the mounted police, as they often passed through the district where Rob lived. However, Rob was convinced that the sounds were made by the horseshoes of some horse pulling a hansom cab, or an old omnibus.

The hypnotic experiments continued with ever-increasing intensity. Rob took to wearing a pair of headphones that fed 'white noise' – gentle static from an FM radio – directly into his ears. Visual distractions to meditation were greatly reduced by wearing the bisected halves of a ping pong ball over both eyes and he must have presented as strange sight to anyone catching him unawares in the middle of one of his meditation sessions. However, the result of his efforts was to create a type of Ganzfield mini-isolation chamber.

On one occasion, while he was meditating, Rob experienced the sensation of falling through a dark void, and a circle opened up in the darkness to reveal a rainy street at night that was lined with gas-lit lampposts. Down the street, as Rob watched, came a plump-looking policeman wearing a cape. Rob inhaled gently, and could plainly detect the aroma of coal fires, the smoke puthering from the numerous chimneys of the Victorian street. Moments later, the scene dissolved back into blackness.

Rob kept a diary of his numerous attempts at mental time travel, and in one entry he wrote that he felt he would soon be sucked back into the past, never to return.

Then, in August 2002, Rob went missing. His parents contacted the police but to no avail, and Rob is still on the missing persons' register. There are a number of possible explanations as to what might have happened to him. He could have suffered some kind of breakdown and left his home in a state of mental confusion. Or perhaps he is trying to perpetrate some kind of hoax, although this would be totally out of character for a man who has never played a prank on anyone in his life. Or did Rob actually achieve his goal, and through the sheer power of the mind, make it back to his beloved romantic age of steam trains, hansom cabs, Jack the Ripper and gas-lit streets?

John has suggested trawling through old newspapers and periodicals of the late nineteenth century to see if there is a mention of anybody strange appearing out of nowhere in old Victorian Liverpool. Perhaps Rob will even turn up, smiling gleefully, from a faded monochrome print in some old-fashioned photograph album.

Strangely enough, in January 2003, John said he was tidying his flat when he came across an old shilling dated 1892, which was in pristine condition. John does not collect old coins, and knows no one who does, so where the shilling came from is a mystery. Unless, it was a sign from an absent friend, a means of indicating that he had finally reached his destination.

Teleportations

Teleportation is the instant relocation of an object or living creature from one place to another, without moving physically across space. A better way of visualising teleportation is to think of Captain Kirk being beamed up to Scotty in the transporter room of the starship *Enterprise* in the original television serial, *Star Trek*. The whole concept of teleportation was once only to be found in the realms of science fiction, but in 1993, a respected physicist, Charles Bennett, and a team of computer experts from IBM, announced to a stunned scientific community, that teleportation was possible at the quantum level of existence.

By 1998, physicists at the California Institute of Technology had successfully teleported a tiny particle of light called a photon. The next step will be to beam molecules, then bacteria and ultimately humans across space in the twinkling of an eye. Air travel and most forms of transportation will become obsolete when the day of the teleporter arrives. However, the annals of the paranormal already contain numerous accounts of teleportation.

In 1620, an eighteen-year-old nun, Mary of Agreda, used to leave her Spanish convent in very mysterious circumstances. She would gradually fade away until she had vanished completely, only to return hours or days later with incredible tales of her adventures on the other side of the world; places that were, at that time, largely unexplored. Mary would frequently tell the other nuns at the convent that she had spent some time among a tribe of primitive people in a country across the Atlantic Ocean, and during her visits she had taught these people all about the teachings of Christ.

Between 1620 and 1631, Mary of Agreda claimed to have made five hundred of these trans-Atlantic jaunts, and the Catholic authorities were decidedly unimpressed by all the tall stories. The Church elders believed that Mary was a self-delusional religious hysteric; that is, until a Christian missionary wrote from the New World with a strange tale.

Father Alonzo de Benavides of the Isolita Mission in New Mexico, wrote to Pope Urban VIII and Philip IV of Spain, asking them who had been visiting the Jumano Indians before him. The Indians in question said that a lady in blue had brought them crosses, rosaries and a chalice which they used to celebrate mass! Father Benavides returned to Spain, and met the 'lady in blue' at the Convent of Agreda, whose habit was indeed blue. The chalice that the Indians had in their possession was found to have belonged to Mary's convent.

*

Nearer to home there have also been reports of inexplicable teleportations, including one that took place between Liscard and Birkenhead. At half-past ten on the wintry evening of Sunday, 25 February 1934, James Johnson, a sixty-year-old plumber, left the Old Nags Head on Rake Lane, Liscard, somewhat the worse for drink. He reached his lodgings at a boarding house that was just three minutes walk away, and after undressing, he slipped on his nightshirt, managed to set the alarm-clock for 7am, then collapsed on his bed, on top of the bedclothes, and promptly fell asleep.

He awoke some time later, shivering in the glacial cold. A light was shining right in his eyes and he could hear voices. As he gradually became more aware of his surroundings, he saw that the voices belonged to two policemen, who were shining a torch at Mr Johnson as he lay on the icy pavement of Slatey Road Birkenhead. The two constables helped him to his feet and started to question him. The plumber was at a loss to explain how he had travelled from his bedroom, still in his nightshirt, the three and a quarter miles to Birkenhead.

Johnson was taken into custody at Slatey Road police station for being drunk and disorderly. At the station, he became even more alarmed and disorientated when he discovered that the time was only five past eleven. The mystery deepened on the following afternoon when Johnson returned to his room at the boarding house, because the landlady told him that she had heard eerie sounds in the his room at around ten to eleven. When she and two other lodgers had gone up to investigate, they got no answer at Johnson's room, upon which they entered the bedroom and found the bed empty and unslept in.

As was common in those times, the incident was deemed to be of a supernatural nature, and James Johnson refused to sleep without a Bible at his bedside from that time on.

*

In 1961, a Mrs Mills entered a Birkenhead shoe shop called England's which was situated on the corner of Grange Road and Coburg Street. Mrs Mills chose a pair of dress shoes for her mother's birthday, but was embarrassed when she discovered that she was half-a-crown short. As she rummaged through her purse, something was seen to fall on to the counter out of thin air. It was a half-a-crown.

When Mrs Mills reached home, she saw that the half-a-crown she had put by on the mantelpiece for her son's pocket money, earlier in the afternoon, had disappeared, yet her son hadn't returned home from school. No one else had access to the house, and Mrs Mills was convinced that the missing coin had somehow travelled to the shop through some benevolent paranormal force, in an effort to spare her the embarrassment of being unable to pay for the shoes.

*

On the other side of the Mersey, in Liverpool, an object was seemingly teleported across time as well as space, by the unconscious summoning of a mind in crisis.

In the district of Waterloo, in July 1979, sixty-nine-year-old Ted Ross retired to his bed at 11pm, and decided to read for a while by the light of the bedside lamp. He dozed off around midnight, but was awakened just before one o'clock by a loud knock at the front door. Ted squinted at the clock, then got out of bed and put on his slippers. He tiptoed down the stairs, stopping to listen every now and then. In the hallway, he caught a fleeting glimpse of a tall figure through the frosted glass panes of his front door. The shadowy night caller moved away from the door as Ted approached. Ted crept into the front parlour and peeked through the net curtains to see a man of about twenty-five, standing inside the front garden. The man then walked across the lawn to an arched passageway that led to the back yard.

Ted was more angry than frightened, and he rushed into his kitchen, and watched as the audacious would-be burglar gazed in. Ted opened the window slightly, startling the young man, and asked him what he thought he was up to. The thief was full of ready answers.

"Oh! Er ... I'm ... er ... the gas man, mate," he faltered, forcing a nervous smile.

"Gas man? It's one in the flippin' morning!" Ted seethed.

"Oh! Er ... erm, we 'ave to come out any time of the day or night, sir. Someone reported smelling gas at this address."

The man seemed to be blindly struggling for an excuse to justify his nocturnal visit and Ted was still convinced that he was a burglar. Nevertheless, he was determined to face up to him, whoever he was, and he angrily flung open the kitchen door. Taking his chance, the burglar rushed in, brandishing a Stanley knife.

"Just say one word, mate, and I'll slice yer face!"

Ted backed away into the hall, wishing he could find something with which to wallop the armed thief. His left hand then located something in the dark corner of the hall, inside the long chrome tube that usually held his umbrella. It was a cricket bat. Ted lifted it almost instinctively and then swung it straight at the burglar's head. The swing was driven by the pure anger he felt at the man's intrusion into his home.

Many years before this incident, Ted had played cricket for an amateur club, and he had been their hardest-hitting batsman. The burglar staggered sideways with the impact, and Ted again lifted the bat high above his head and started to whack the hand that held the knife. The burglar screamed out for Ted to stop, and he scrambled to his feet but, just before he fled, the bat struck him hard across the buttocks. Ted shut the kitchen door and bolted it, then went into the hall and telephoned the police. The police soon turned up and a detective told Ted that a series of burglaries had been committed across Waterloo, and they had several suspects in the frame already. A week later the man who had threatened Ted with the knife was arrested and subsequently jailed.

When Ted thought about the incident later, he was baffled at the sudden appearance of the old cricket bat, which was identical to the one he had once treasured in the late 1930s. It was an old bat that had belonged to his father, who had also been a keen amateur cricketer. The cherished handmade bat had the name of the top scorer inscribed on it, and Ted had never had the bat's handle rewound. Shortly before the outbreak of World War Two, the bat was mislaid and had never been seen again until the night of the burglary. The bat that had seemingly appeared out of nowhere in Ted's hall had saved his life, and Ted was sure that the bat had somehow been sent to him from his father, from beyond the grave, or 'at the far end', to use cricketing parlance.

Haunted Objects

The following two tales are about inanimate objects that were apparently haunted …

In the 1930s, forty-five-year-old John Negus was employed as a crane operator at Storeton quarry in Bebington. The high quality stones which were hewn from the quarry were not only used locally to build the magnificent villas around Birkenhead Park. So highly prised was Storeton stone that it was also exported to New York, to clad the world famous Empire State building.

During the continuous excavations and chiselling at Storeton quarry in 1935, it is said that a strange artefact was unearthed. It was a peculiar black comb, made of some marble-like material, and it had just nine teeth. Instead of handing over the apparently stone-aged comb to archaeologists, John Negus took it home to his house in Rock Ferry. Negus showed his wife Teresa the comb, and without touching it, she told him to throw it away. Teresa was psychic, and she detected that the black comb gave off eerie impressions of death and evil. John Negus dismissed his wife's alleged psychical skills as so much mumbo jumbo – "sikey mumbo jumbo" – he called them. He felt that they were just the result of Teresa's having been brought up by an eccentric, superstitious mother and a fanatically religious father.

That night though, John Negus had a strange dream about the comb. In the dream he could see a woman with long blonde hair sitting on a stool in some old dark room. The woman was leaning forward, with her hair covering her face, and she was combing her locks with the very comb that John had brought home from the quarry. As John looked on, he intuitively knew that the woman would kill him as soon as she stopped combing her hair. His conviction was soon proved to be true; the woman in black started to comb more and more slowly and then suddenly she raised the comb above her head, where it metamorphosed into a long-bladed knife. As she prepared to throw the knife at John, he yelled out and woke up in a cold sweat.

That same terrifying nightmare replayed itself three times more that night in the crane operator's dreaming mind. In the end, John refused to go back to sleep, because he knew that if the woman succeeded in throwing the knife at him, he would die in his sleep from the shock. John's wife Teresa pleaded with her husband to throw away the accursed comb – this time John readily agreed – but when he got out of bed to look for it, he couldn't find the ancient relic. It transpired that his nine-year-old son had been playing with the comb somewhere in the house and had mislaid it. John and Teresa searched high and low but were unable to find the haunted object.

John sat up in bed, trembling, as sleep insidiously crept over him. He described in great detail to his wife how he had seen the comb turn into a knife in the woman's hand, and how she had hurled it at him. The knife had been in mid-air as he had awakened just in time.

Teresa begged her husband to sleep at her mother's house that night, but John would hear none of it, and he wondered if the dreams were a sign that he was losing his mind. At three in the morning, Teresa dozed off for a while, and when she woke, she felt the cold empty space beside her. She assumed that her husband had either taken her advice and left the house to sleep at her mother's, or had gone downstairs to sit up until morning. Then she found him – lying motionless on the floor beside the bed, and she became hysterical. John Negus was laying on his back, his eyes staring in abject terror at the ceiling, and his hands clutching at his chest. He was dead.

It is said that the black comb was found not long afterwards at the Negus household, and that it has changed hands and claimed lives many times, and is now in the Liverpool area. Over and over again I have heard the tale of the terrifying dream that features the lady combing her hair with a comb that changes into a knife. If you can wake yourself up before she stops combing you're safe – otherwise, the comb turns into a knife and she throws it at your chest, impaling the heart in one expert throw – and you die in your sleep.

*

Another object that seemingly had a ghost attached to it was an old Metropolitan Police whistle and chain, purchased from a Liverpool antique shop in the 1990s. Stan did not believe in ghosts or entertain the notion of a spirit world. He was a dedicated materialist who hoarded antiques and Victoriana. He was a regular visitor to the bric-a-brac stalls in Quiggins, and the auctioneers Outhwaite and Litherland in Liverpool's Fontenoy Street, in the heart of the city.

In 1998, Stan purchased an old walnut police truncheon and a police constable's whistle and chain. They had belonged to a Liverpool policeman named Edwards who had served in London's Metropolitan police force until 1899, when he died from a blood clot on the brain, aged fifty-five.

In July 1998, Stan took the policeman's whistle and truncheon to his home in

Quarry Street, Woolton Hill. On the following Saturday night, Stan and his wife went out for a meal with some of their friends to a restaurant in Liverpool city centre, and they left their seventeen-year-old son Dale, and his sixteen-year-old girlfriend Andrea at home.

The teenaged couple initially entertained themselves by playing games on the television with a play station, but at around half-past ten, Dale went upstairs to mooch about in the room in which his father kept his antiques, and he found the policeman's whistle. Andrea soon followed him up there. Dale stood on the window ledge of the antiques room, and opened the windows wide. He blew on the old police whistle as hard as he could, startling a man down in the street below who was walking his bulldog. Dale and Andrea laughed as the jowly brute gazed upwards with a fixed stare at their mischievous faces peering though the window. It growled and barked furiously, and its owner had to drag it away. Andrea then experimented with the whistle, but soon tired of it. She then closed the window and went back downstairs into the lounge.

She and Dale were about to settle down to watch a programme on television when the automatic anti-prowler light at the front of the house flashed on, flooding the driveway with light. Dale and Andrea listened to the steady footfall of someone walking up the gravel drive towards the house. Dale assumed that it was one of his parents returning early for some reason, but when he peeped through the blinds he quickly realised that the person outside was neither his mother nor his father. A tall, helmeted policeman, wearing some sort of cape, was standing on the drive. His face looked ashen, almost as if he was wearing pale make up, and it contrasted starkly with the large black walrus moustache he wore. He looked outdated and eerie.

Andrea took a peek through the blinds at the strange figure, and trembled as he came right up to the window. Dale muted the television with the remote control, dimmed the lights and froze. The odd-looking policeman rapped twice on the window with his knuckles and muttered something unintelligible. Dale and Andrea watched the shadow of the constable's head and shoulders glide slowly across the blinds as he walked past the window. The dull thumps of his heavy boots faded until there was an uneasy silence.

Twenty minutes later, a hackney cab pulled up outside, and Dale's parents came up the drive. The young couple breathed a sigh of relief Stan listened to his son's strange account of the antiquated officer of the law – and he knew him well enough to know when he was lying. He looked badly shaken, as did Andrea.

Only on the following morning did Dale admit to blowing the old police whistle, and immediately, his mother wondered if the blowing of the Victorian whistle had somehow conjured up the ghost of its deceased owner. Stan thought his wife was being fanciful, and thought the policeman had just been some kind of prankster – he'd probably been on the way home from a fancy dress party or something. However, Stan asked a friend to discover just where PC Edwards, the owner of the whistle and truncheon, had lived shortly before his death. It turned out that he had lived off Quarry Street, just a few houses away from Stan.

Stan still couldn't accept that the old silver remnant had somehow summoned a long-dead policeman, but despite Dale's persistent requests, the sceptical antiques hoarder refused to blow on the whistle – just in case.

Mr Sphinx

One stormy evening at Woolton Hall in 2003, I gave an illustrated talk on the subject of the supernatural, which included several tales on the subject of vampires. After the talk, Susan, a distinguished-looking woman of eighty, approached me and told me how much she had enjoyed the stories and slide show pictures. She then related an intriguing story of her own that was as good, if not better, than any of the tales I'd been telling to people that evening. This is the account she gave.

Susan was born in Northumberland in 1923, and her mother, a teacher of English and Latin, brought Susan to Liverpool in 1933. Susan's father had deserted her mother just before the girl's birth. In the leafy lanes of suburban Aigburth, ten-year-old Susan and her mother settled into a beautiful house on Waverley Road. However, the rent for the fine residence was barely covered by the money Susan's mother brought in from her job as a private tutor.

In the autumn of 1933, a tall, smartly-dressed stranger with coal-black hair and penetrating green eyes called at the house, and told Susan's mother, in a foreign accent, that he would like to learn how to speak English. The man's name, Raymond Sphinx, struck Susan as being rather odd to say the least. Susan's mother explained that many foreigners choose their own names to replace their real, exotic-sounding surnames, in order to blend in to the country they are living in. Mr Sphinx was quite handsome, and as Susan related this tale, she recalled how her mother seemed totally mesmerised by the debonair foreigner, who seemed to be about thirty-five years of age. He was so courteous and sophisticated, and must have been an excellent student, as he was soon speaking with a fine, mellifluous English accent.

Children are very perceptive and discerning when it comes to seeing through the pretensions of adults, and young Susan thought there was something decidedly uncanny about Mr Sphinx. He seemed to appear out of nowhere whenever he visited for his lessons, and throughout the early summer of 1934, Susan watched him walk out on to a veranda – and when she followed, he had vanished. When she mentioned this to her mother, she was accused of having an overactive imagination.

Some time later though, Susan's mother said she too had seen Raymond walk on to the veranda and then seemingly disappear into thin air. She even mentioned the incident to him on the following day, but he just smiled his enigmatic smile and said that he had slipped past her but she hadn't noticed him. Susan's mother said nothing, but knew that simply had not been the case at all.

Mr Sphinx continued to come to the house, long after he needed to, as he now spoke English as perfectly as Susan's mother. Then it slowly dawned on Susan that her mother was romantically involved with the foreigner, and on many nights she would listen to him as he sat at the piano in the drawing room, bringing forth soul-stirring concertos of Mozart and Beethoven. Some of the other, unknown melodies sounded mysterious and romantic, and they brought tears to the eyes of Susan's mother.

The multi-talented Mr Sphinx was also an amazing storyteller, and on winter evenings he would sit before a blazing coal fire with Susan by his side and tell her tales of kings, queens, and ordinary people of long ago. He would also describe the daring missions of King Arthur and his Knights of the Round Table, and a saga about two young lovers on opposing sides during the Wars of the Roses. Raymond told these stories with such skill, that his listeners almost believed they were actually there, in the midst of the romance and intrigue.

Susan's mother's liking for Mr Sphinx must have waned, because she became involved with another man in 1936, and Raymond decided to leave but, before he went, he produced a single blood-red rose, backed with maidenhair fern and gave it to thirteen-year-old Susan, who was heart-broken at the idea of him leaving her life. Raymond whispered the word 'Zuzana' – an old Slavic word for the rose – and said that he would return one day when she was older, and declared that his love for her was undying. He said that the rose he had given her would never die, just like the affection he felt for her. With a tear in his eye, he said, "Remember me," then left, and Susan began to sob. She begged her mother to leave her lover and to resume her relationship with Raymond, but to no avail.

The rose which Mr Sphinx had given to Susan refused to wilt, and she kept it in a special box. World War Two came and went, and still the red rose and maidenhair fern looked as fresh as the day he had given them to her.

In 1948, at the age of twenty-five, Susan married a thirty-one-year-old man named Ralph, and moved with him just around the corner from her mother, to live over the grocery shop he owned. Susan's mother was ill at this time, and her condition was exacerbated by the anger she felt towards Susan for "marrying beneath herself" as she put it, and the heartbreak she was enduring because her lover had deserted her for a much younger woman.

Weeks later, Susan's mother died from pulmonary complications, and only Susan, Ralph and a doctor were at her bedside. About a fortnight after the funeral, Susan went to the cemetery alone to place flowers on her mother's grave, and during the visit she had an encounter that initially shocked her. A tall man dressed in black was already standing at the foot of her mother's grave. He turned as Susan approached. It was Raymond Sphinx, and he looked as if he hadn't aged a day since she last saw him in 1936, twelve years ago. He stood there with a faint smile on his lips; his arms outstretched to embrace Susan. He hugged and kissed her, and offered his deepest condolences. He assured her that her mother had merely shed her physical body, and that her soul had gone on to another plane of existence, where every person ends up when earthly life ceases.

Susan felt an intense physical and romantic attraction to Raymond, and she asked him to accompany her to her late mother's home on Waverley Road. At the house where Raymond had first met Susan as a child, she showed him the box containing the undying rose. Raymond embraced Susan and kissed her passionately. Not long afterwards they were making love, and throughout the act, Susan felt all her energy steadily draining away.

When the couple had finished making love, Susan felt numb and empty, and so listless, she could hardly make the effort to draw breath. A strange thought crossed her lethargic mind: had Raymond somehow siphoned off the very essence of her life force? Her lover leaned on his elbow beside her, and scanned her face, then put his palm on her forehead. Susan felt a distinct sensation of something in flux passing between his hand and her mind. Energy flowed down her spine and a strange cold tingling sensation coursed down her arms and legs.

After a while, Raymond removed his palm and then kissed Susan's cheek. She raised herself up and asked him what had just happened. She was more fascinated than afraid. She had never experienced such intense electric pleasures when her husband had made love to her. What Raymond told her shocked her to her core. Sphinx explained that he was a "type of vampire". He was nothing like the Dracula character of the Bram Stoker novel. He didn't suck blood, but he did "feed" off the life force of people – 'prana'.

Susan found herself putting on her dress without bothering to put on her underwear first. She trembled as Raymond sat at end of the bed with his head bowed and knew that he wasn't mentally unbalanced. She also knew he wasn't just trying to frighten her – he was telling the truth – she could tell by that look of sincerity in his green eyes.

"Please don't go, Susan," he said meekly.

The everlasting rose flashed into her mind. Of course! – now it all made sense. All those tales of long ago that Raymond had told around the fireside when she was a child. No wonder he had been able to make them sound so realistic – he must have been walking the earth for hundreds of years! Was he some kind of devil?

Susan didn't stop to look back as she hurried out of the bedroom in a panic, clutching her shoes. She walked barefooted down the road and only put the shoes on once she had turned the corner, from where she walked in shock back to her home above the greengrocer's. Ralph didn't even notice that her hair was in disarray, her lipstick smudged and her clothes dishevelled. Susan didn't return to her former home on Waverley Road until the next day, and when she did, she made sure that a friend went with her. She need not have worried – Raymond had gone.

In 1977, at the age of fifty-four, Susan was out shopping in Liverpool city centre when, just as she was leaving Binn's department store, she came face to face with Raymond. He still looked around thirty-five, with not a single wrinkle on his handsome face, or grey hair on his head. His green eyes sparkled as keenly as ever. He didn't recognise her at first, and he walked on past – but then he hesitated, and turned around. Not a word was spoken for a frozen moment in time. Then, as if he hadn't seen Susan for just a few days, he asked her how she was, and reached out for her hand – but Susan pulled away. He then suggested going to a nearby café, but Susan resolutely shook her head. Raymond seemed to sense that she was worried over something, and asked if her husband was well. Susan didn't answer. Instead, she turned and walked away, as Raymond shouted her name three times. She resolutely ignored him and walked away towards the safety of the crowds milling in and out of Woolworths.

In the Northern Hospital that evening, Susan's husband Ralph was lying in a bed, drifting in and out of a comatose state with a blood clot on his brain. The doctors had told Susan that he was in a critical condition and there was a high probability that he would not pull through. It had already been explained to her that brain surgery would be far too risky in Ralph's weakened condition.

At home, Susan fastened the top and bottom bolts of the front door, and locked her back door. Not only was she totally distraught about her husband's grave condition, but also deeply troubled about the meeting with Raymond, after all those years. She also wondered if the eerie Raymond had somehow followed her home. She took an old Bible up to the bedroom and sat up in bed, listening to the radio. She reached for the old Bible and opened it at random. She scanned a passage about the transfiguration of Christ, and for some reason it made her think about Raymond. With shame, she recalled the strange, unearthly sensations she had experienced when she was in the bed with him all those years ago, and of that mysterious word he spoke – 'prana'.

At almost three in the morning, Susan drifted into a fitful sleep that was haunted by dreams of Raymond. At eight o'clock the bell of the alarm clock sounded, and she swung her legs out of the bed like an automaton, with her eyelids still stuck together. With a sinking feeling in the pit of her stomach, she went downstairs to the hall, still in her nightdress, and telephoned the hospital. She feared the worst and dreaded to hear what they would say about her husband's condition.

She was in for a massive shock. The sister on duty said that she had some very good news. Ralph was no longer on the critical list; in fact, he was sitting up in bed, eating a hearty breakfast and laughing and joking with all the nurses. He had made a recovery that was nothing short of miraculous.

Susan was dressed and ready within half an hour of hearing this wonderful news and was soon riding in a cab to the hospital. Bursting with excitement, she rushed into the room where Ralph had lain at the gates of death for almost a month … and found the bed empty. The other bed in that room, in which a young man had been recovering from a spinal injury, was also vacant. Then she heard the sound of footsteps in the corridor to her right. It was Ralph, walking along with a nurse on either side of him, supporting him as he walked along. When he saw Susan he stopped in his tracks, and she ran to him with tears welling in her eyes. She hugged him so tightly, and he kept saying, "There, there, love," as he patted her on the back.

The nurses seemed to be just as overjoyed as they were – such miraculous recoveries happened so rarely. They showed Susan and Ralph into the two-bed ward, then left to give them some privacy. Ralph told Susan a tale that made her stomach somersault. He said that a "funny-looking man" had come into his room some time after midnight. He had walked over to Pete – the young man who was lying asleep in the other bed – and had placed his hands on the young man's chest. Ralph had been barely conscious, and the whole thing had a dream-like quality. The man – who was dressed in black – then came over to Ralph's bed and placed his palms on his chest. The intense heat from the stranger's hands penetrated right through his pyjamas, and his vest, straight into his heart. Ralph felt his entire body tingling, as if he had been plugged into the electricity mains. The man then assured Ralph that he would get better soon, then left the room in absolute silence – just like a ghost.

At six o'clock in the morning, Ralph opened his eyes, feeling like a new man. He sat up, stretched and yawned, and found a Catholic priest, a doctor and three relatives surrounding the bed of the man opposite, who was obviously dying. The priest was performing the Last Rites and Pete died soon afterwards.

"You don't believe me, do you?" Ralph said to Susan, who was staring at the single red rose, backed with a stem of maidenhead fern, lying on the bedside cabinet.

She knew exactly what had happened. Raymond – or whatever his real name was – had siphoned off the life of the young man in the other bed, and had infused that life into Ralph. Why had he done this? Susan still doesn't have any answers to this question.

Before Susan left Woolton Hall that stormy night, she told me that she was convinced that Mr Sphinx was still around.

"He will probably visit you if you put him in one of your books," she told me.

She then bade me goodnight, and a hackney cab took her off into the night.

Early Air-Mail?

In March 1856, a strange whistling sound was heard in the early morning skies over Hooton, Wirral. A farmer in the area named Graves told people he saw a strange white object drifting high over a field, and when he went in search of it, he found nothing resembling the object, only a band of mysterious strangers dressed in black, who warned the farmer to keep away from the wood behind them.

A week later, something else fell from the sky on to southern Wirral, about a quarter of a mile south of Hooton. At seven o'clock in the morning, an old woman at Childer Thornton heard a thunderous explosion in the garden of her cottage, and when she went outside to find out what had caused the blast, she found pieces of metal and shredded paper scattered everywhere. Unfortunately, the old woman was illiterate, and so she was unable to make head or tail of the torn pieces of documents spread across her property.

Stranger still, a group of men who claimed they were detectives, later turned up at the cottage and painstakingly collected all the pieces of paper and fragments of metal, down to the last tiny fragments. It was as if an artillery shell, laden with a bundle of papers, had exploded on impact with the ground.

A month later, another mysterious projectile whistled at a hypersonic velocity towards the north of Wirral, and it came from the direction of Bootle. Fishermen on the Wallasey coast saw something plunge into the sea and throw up a great quantity of spray.

Mysterious explosions have been heard in other parts of the world. Throughout the nineteenth century, deafening booms of unknown origin were heard regularly throughout the Ganges Delta in India, and were nicknamed the Guns of Barisal (a port in the Bay of Bengal).

Closer to home, the sailors of the Mersey were well aware of the equally mysterious 'mist pouffers' – uncanny thundering sounds which came from nowhere and bombarded their ears in the middle of the ocean. Most of the sailors at Liverpool docks and the inhabitants of the Wirral who had heard the strange explosions and whistling sounds in 1856, thought that they were some kind of supernatural phenomenon, but the truth seems to be somewhat more mundane, but intriguing nevertheless.

In 1856, brilliant Mancunian, Joseph Whitworth, was building various mortars, cannons and military guns at the Vauxhall foundry in Liverpool. On 6 May 1856, Whitworth had his giant hexagonal gun rolled down to the shore at Bootle in order to show it off to the assembled members of the military. A twenty-four-pound metal ball was fired, but went off course in its trajectory and came down in Waterloo, where it cut down a tree, before entering the parlour window of a merchant named Houghton. The cannon ball scattered the merchant's furniture and impacted into an internal wall, but fortunately no one was injured.

John Jones, another genius working with Whitworth, had a grand plan to put mail and parcels into a shell-shaped cartridge that could be fired across the Mersey to the Wirral peninsula. Such 'ballistic mail' would almost be as fast as a modern email but, unlike email, the mail delivered by Whitworth's gun could also include parcels. A parachute would possibly have been deployed once the shell had traversed a given distance on its parabolic path. Does all this explain the strange projectiles that fell on Wirral in 1856, scattering metal and paper in their wake?

The Ones that Got Away

By no means all of the local mysteries I research are satisfactorily solved. Take the mystery of the 'Aintree Iron', an enigmatic slang phrase for something that has never been identified. The pop group Scaffold alluded to the Aintree Iron in their 1968 song *Thank U Very Much* – and in doing so, brought an old phrase out of mothballs that hadn't been in common usage in years. An 'Iron hoof' was rhyming slang for a homosexual, and some thought the Aintree Iron was referring to a certain manager of a very successful pop group in the 1960s, who hailed from Aintree, whereas other Liverpudlians argued that the Iron was a reference to the two train lines running through Aintree that resembled the outline of a giant flat iron when viewed from an aerial perspective. Some even said the Iron was obviously the world famous racecourse, but the various interpretations and speculations continue even today.

Another unsolved mystery concerns Aintree Racecourse and Devon Loch, the

Queen Mother's horse, which was galloping down the home straight, set to win the Grand National in March 1956, when suddenly, for no apparent reason, it belly-flopped and skidded to a halt, just fifty yards away from the winning post. People swore that the horse had tried to jump over the shadow of a fence and had lost its footing, whilst others believed that it was the roar of the crowd cheering the horse on, that had frightened it. Devon Loch's dramatic, inexplicable collapse remains one of the greatest racing conundrums of the turf.

Another mystery that has tantalisingly resurfaced again and again is the cold-blooded massacre of the school of stranded whales in the River Mersey. There is definitely some grain of truth in this story, no matter how far-fetched it seems, as so many level-headed people from all walks of life have emailed the story to me, or written to me via 'snail mail'. Some have even visited me in person, either at radio stations, or at my lectures, and told me how they were present at the barbaric culling. All the tales agree that the atrocity took place some time in the late 1950s.

One beautiful sunny Sunday afternoon, around 1959, large numbers of people were strolling along Otterspool Promenade, enjoying the scenery and the fresh air, when they noticed, in the distance, a row of black glistening humps, slowly moving down the River Mersey. The humps were actually three or four whales, and a small naval ship of some sort was pursuing them. One of the larger whales then veered away from the others towards the shore, and people on the promenade gasped in amazement – whale watching was not something they had expected to be doing on a quiet Sunday afternoon down at the prom. Children jumped up and down with excitement and the crowd of watchers grew, as all those who had been picknicking on the banks rushed down to the riverside.

Suddenly the crowds scattered as a number of army jeeps came roaring down the river-front esplanade, and a military man on one of the jeeps used a megaphone to order people out of the way and off the promenade. The startled strollers ran in every direction and watched in horror from the top of the grassy banks as soldiers with rifles leapt out of the jeeps and took up firing positions along the railings. In no time, they had begun firing on the isolated whale which was now helplessly beached on the muddy sandflats at the low water mark. Mothers shielded their children's eyes, and fathers shook their heads in abhorrence and disbelief at the butchery they were being forced to witness. Before long, great torrents of the mighty mammal's blood were gushing from the dozens of bullet holes which riddled its body, spreading out across the sand and turning the murky waters a deep reddish brown colour.

Meanwhile, down at Hale Bank and Widnes, the army were busy firing volleys of shots at the other whales. At first, a rumour went round that the soldiers were firing upon an old unexploded sea mine left over from World War Two that was presenting a threat to shipping, but soon people in the area realised that the firepower was actually directed at the helpless whales. Once the carnage was over, the stricken carcasses of the whales were then unceremoniously hauled off to a dog-food factory near Fiddler's Ferry, leaving a long trail of blood, like a stain of shame on the River Mersey.

Whales have been stranded in the Mersey before; one as recently as August 1998, when one got into trouble at Hale Bank.

If you can throw any light on these, or any other of these solution-resistant mysteries, please contact me!

Spanner Face

Lots of people touch the nearest piece of wood when they think they have just tempted fate with some comment such as, "The doctor says my husband is recovering well and he'll be out of hospital tomorrow – touch wood."

In America they say "knock wood" after untimely boasting. The touching of wood after tempting fate is a ritual lost in the mists of time, but some researchers into superstitions have noted pre-Christian rituals involving the hugging of trees that were regarded as sacred, such as oak, ash, holly or hawthorn. And in Ireland there is an old tongue-in-cheek tradition of knocking on wood to let the little people know that you are thanking them for any good luck received.

One of the most gruesome incidents of someone tempting fate took place in Liverpool in the 1960s. Twenty-five-year-old Joan Dymond was said to have been the most beautiful woman in Liverpool at the time. The year was 1963, and Joan was living off Mill Street in south Liverpool. People who remember Joan claim that she could easily have ended up as a Hollywood movie star – perhaps after a few lessons in elocution. Joan's good looks attracted men of every age and type – but mostly the wrong type!

Despite being able to take her pick, in the summer of 1963, she married a violent former teddy boy from Huyton named Terry; a man well known to the Liverpool and Lancashire police. Joan's parents and friends had pleaded with her to call off the marriage to a man whose infamy was known across the county, but the wedding went ahead anyway – such is the blindness of youth. The marriage couldn't have got off to a worse start, because, even during the wedding reception, Terry head-butted his own brother because of some mild insult he was supposed to have made. By the end of August, Joan had received several beatings at the hands of Terry, usually after he had returned home drunk, in the early hours of the morning.

Beaten and bruised, Joan eventually ran back home to her parents, but even there she found no sanctuary, because Terry booted in the door of their home on one occasion and threatened her father with a knife. After this incident, Joan was given shelter at the Anne Fowler Memorial Home for Women on Netherfield Road. It was the last refuge for many beaten wives who had no place left to run. Terry wrote numerous pleading letters to Joan, telling her how much he had changed, and how he had now learnt to control his violent streak. He assured her that he hadn't touched a drop of alcohol for over a fortnight and wanted nothing more than to settle down with her in a cottage in Wales. Each night he prayed for God to give him a second chance – or so he claimed in his floridly-phrased letters.

Despite the cracked rib he had given her, and the black eye, and the dislocated jaw – Joan went back to Terry, like so many battered wives before her. He was elated at the reconciliation, and after showering her with flowers, chocolates, gifts and new clothes, he took Joan out in his new car. They went on the town to celebrate, and Terry was the envy of every hot-blooded male, because he once more had the beautiful goddess Joan on his arm.

The couple pushed their way into the crowded Grapes pub on Mathew Street, and Terry barged his way to the bar counter, with Joan clutching at his hand. A tall, quietly spoken college student standing at the bar was sipping a glass of sarsparilla, and when Terry rudely knocked him sideways, the student protested.

"Hey, mate. What d'you think you're doing?"

"Outside, come on!" Terry bawled, "No one talks to me like that."

"Very well," said the student, calmly placing his glass of sarsparilla on the counter and making his way to the door.

Terry was taken aback by the student's lack of nerves. He watched him leave the pub, and was about to follow him through the door, when a friend of his warned him not to go. He told Terry that the student was a brilliant amateur middle-weight boxer who fought for his college. Terry took off his knuckleduster, and after pondering on the situation for a minute or two, bought a pint of sarsparilla and told his friend to take it outside to the student. The student luckily saw the funny side of the gesture and came back into the pub smiling. Joan, who had been cringing in a corner, breathed a sigh of relief; it was turning into a good night with no violence for once.

During the evening, Terry even took part in a few arm-wrestling competitions, and didn't take it personally when he lost. By ten-thirty, he was sitting in a corner of the pub with a drunken Joan sitting on his knee, and they were laughing and singing. There was a sudden lull in the noisy chatter of the pub. The singing stopped, the conversationalists fell silent, and the laughter ceased. Something was moving through the pub, among the drinkers. It was something that cackled. It wore a headscarf, and it sidled over to the corner where Joan and Terry were sitting – it was Spanner Face.

Joan was almost struck sober at the horrific sight and Terry gasped with revulsion. The woman with the headscarf had a grossly disfigured face. The forehead and chin protruded like the points of a crescent moon, and the face was concave and mostly absent. Viewed side on, the face was C-shaped, like the gripping end of a spanner, hence the unfortunate woman's cruel nickname. She muttered something to Joan and Terry but neither heard her words, as they were too overwhelmed by the deformity of her face.

"Can you spare a woodbine, my dears?" she said once more, holding out her hand.

"God almighty! What happened to your face, love?" Terry asked, hoping for a cheap laugh at the poor woman's expense. He attempted a false belly laugh, but the hush around the premises was almost deafening, and his laugh died away, to be replaced with an embarrassed smile. Everyone looked away from the woman.

At last the silence was broken when Joan hid her face in Terry's jacket and giggled nervously.

"Funny isn't it?" Terry remarked, addressing the silent drinkers, "We've got the most beautiful girl in Liverpool and the ugliest old hag in Liverpool in the same pub."

"You're tempting fate, mister," said the unsightly woman under her breath.

Then door opened and in came a youth in high spirits, singing a Beatles hit. He looked around at the subdued drinkers, and saw that most of them were staring down into their glasses, "Who's died? Is this a bleedin' wake or something?"

Spanner Face turned abruptly and walked out the door, passing the hapless youth who rapidly stepped out of her way when he glimpsed the awful sight under the headscarf. There was a stir of conversation, and within less than a minute, the laughter, chatting and singing had been resumed to form the usual din in the smoky atmosphere. Terry enquired about the disfigured woman, and a few people shook their heads and explained that she was a gypsy of some sort who brought bad luck, unless you gave her what she asked for. They nervously told Terry that the woman's nickname was Spanner Face, but Terry and Joan didn't smile when they heard this.

At three o'clock that morning, Joan woke up with an agonising pain in one of her back teeth. She opened her mouth wide and peered into the bathroom mirror. She was alarmed to find that there was blood oozing from the gums around the aching tooth. She took some painkillers, but they made no difference, and the toothache was soon excruciating. Terry plied her with a concoction of milk and rum, but it too did nothing to alleviate the pain, and Joan started to cry.

She had to endure the terrible agony all over the weekend, but early on Monday morning, Terry drove her to the dentist's surgery. The dentist took a quick look at the back tooth and immediately recoiled.

"I'm afraid this is serious," he said.

"What do you mean?" Joan asked, her beautiful eyes brimming with tears.

"Please, just go at once to the hospital. Go there now as soon as you can. I'm afraid it looks like gangrene," said the dentist.

Terry sped through red traffic lights to get his wife to the hospital. When Joan told a nurse about the dentist's comments, she was taken at once into a room to be examined by a surgeon. He looked as shocked as the dentist when he shone a light into Joan's mouth.

Within the hour, Joan's parents had arrived at the hospital. They sat with Terry in a waiting room, chain smoking and trying to take in the graveness of the situation.

Forms were signed by Terry, giving the surgeon permission to operate on Joan, who by now was in no fit state to give her own consent, having been given morphine. Joan's parents asked the surgeon to explain why he had to operate, and he told them that gangrene from tooth decay had caused a life-threatening abscess to form. It was imperative that the gangrene be removed as soon as possible to stop it from spreading throughout Joan's bloodstream, which would kill her.

Joan was wheeled into theatre and the hours dragged by without any word for her anxious relatives. Then, after a gruelling eight hours, the operation finally ended. The gangrenous area had been removed – but at a terrible cost. Joan's parents and Terry were told to go home and rest, as Joan would not be conscious or well enough to receive visitors for a while.

Two days later, Joan's mother and father tiptoed into the small private room to see their daughter for the first time since the operation, but all they could see was an inert figure lying on the bed, with a face completely bandaged like an Egyptian mummy. Terry visited later in the day but couldn't elicit a single spoken response from his wife. Three days later, Joan's parents and Terry were present at Joan's bedside when the bandages were changed, and all three went into shock when they saw what the radical surgery had done to her beautiful face. Entire chunks of it were missing, and most of the lower jaw had been hacked away. Joan's mother fainted at the sight of the disfigurement, and Terry was glad that she had collapsed, because it gave him an excuse to leave the room as he carried her out into the corridor.

What little remained of Joan's face was unrecognisable and yet looked chillingly familiar somehow. Then it slowly dawned on Terry that she now looked exactly like Spanner Face, the old woman who had approached them in the pub on the very night that Joan had been taken ill.

"Terry, please stay with her," pleaded Joan's mother when she came to. "You won't leave her, will you?"

Without answering, Terry, true to form, callously turned his back on the stricken woman and walked straight down the long corridor and right out of the hospital, already thinking about divorce, and starting afresh with a new partner. When he reached the gates of the hospital, he saw an old flower seller, who slowly turned to face him – it was Spanner Face. She cackled horribly as he hurried away.

The once lovely Joan eventually recovered her health, but lived the rest of her life shut away at her parents' home on Windsor Street, unable to face the world with her terrible disfigurement. She is thought to have died in the early 1980s.

The Ghostly Aviator of Dacre Hill

In March 1979, Frank and Maureen, a couple in their forties from the Kirkby area of Liverpool, went to live at Dacre Hill, near Rock Ferry. Maureen worked at a shop in Birkenhead, and Frank held a job at a Port Sunlight factory.

The couple soon settled into their three-bedroom terraced home – that is, until one rainy night in April 1979. Tired after a hard day's work, they climbed into bed at midnight, and before Maureen could switch off the bedside lamp, Frank fell fast asleep. Maureen yawned, and reached out to switch off the lamp – when she thought she heard voices. She shook Frank awake, and in a grumbling voice he asked what the matter was.

"Listen …" Maureen whispered.

Frank didn't even open his weary eyes, and started to drift back off into the sleep he valued so much. Maureen strained her ears, and listened to the slow gentle footsteps on the stairs. Without a doubt, someone was coming up to the bedroom. The gentle thuds of the eerie midnight walker halted right outside the bedroom door.

Maureen froze. The door knob squeaked faintly as it turned. The door slowly opened – Maureen was still paralysed with fear. She couldn't scream, nor could she shake her husband awake. The only light coming into the room were the orange rays from a lamp-post, filtering through the drawn curtains, but even by that subdued light, Maureen could make out a man, about six feet tall, entering the room. He wore a type of helmet with goggles, a waist-length leather jacket, and dark trousers. He looked for all the world like some old-fashioned aeroplane pilot. Maureen felt as if she was in some terrifying nightmare from which she couldn't awaken.

The aviator walked slowly towards her side of the bed with a smile on his sinister pale face. Maureen tried to close her eyes, but she found she couldn't even shut her eyelids. The pilot leaned over her and put his gloved hand over her mouth. His face was about five inches away from hers, and Maureen was gazing directly into the dark menacing eyes. She suddenly heard the distinctive drone of aeroplanes, then heard what sounded like the screeching descent of a plane in trouble. The sound got louder and louder, deafeningly loud, as if the plane was about to fall on to the house.

As if some kind of spell had been broken, in an instant, Maureen closed her eyes, pushed away the leather gloved hand, and let out an ear-piercing scream. The aviator was suddenly gone, and Frank was sitting bolt upright in bed. Maureen clung to him, shaking, and Frank asked her what the matter was. He assumed his wife had experienced some kind of nightmare, but she told him about the creepy man dressed as a pilot who had tried to suffocate her by pressing his hand over her mouth.

Frank, now alert and full of adrenalin, reached under the bed and grabbed the hammer he kept especially for burglars, then went in search of the intruder. He returned minutes later, saying that there was no sign of anyone having broken in, and he finally managed to convince Maureen that she had merely had an abnormally realistic nightmare. Nevertheless, it was two in the morning before Maureen finally calmed down sufficiently to fall asleep.

A few weeks later, Maureen returned home late from Liverpool to find Frank frantically stripping the wallpaper off their bedroom walls. Frank, who hated any form of DIY and usually had to be nagged into doing any decorating. So Maureen naturally asked him why on earth he was stripping the walls at half-past-eleven at night. Frank wouldn't answer at first, but just carried on stripping the walls as if his life depended on it. However, later, downstairs in the kitchen, he mentioned something strange over a cup of tea that turned Maureen cold.

Apparently, Frank had returned from the pub earlier in the evening, at about ten o'clock. Whilst sitting on the bed to take off his boots, he thought he saw a dark shape flit across the facing wall. He had been drinking a potent wine earlier called Bentox, and a friend had convinced him to also drink a few pints of bitter. Frank therefore thought he was having some kind of alcohol-induced hallucination when more dark shapes flitted across the wallpaper.

Deciding that the best place for someone in his state was in bed, he undressed, climbed under the covers and closed his eyes. However, he was soon startled by what sounded like the deep chuckling of someone close by. He looked around the room and reassured himself that there was no one there. The sound of laughter must have drifted into the room from someone out in the night street, he reasoned. Then Frank glanced at the section of the wall illuminated by the orange light from the street lamp. The dark shapes were back on the wall.

Frank slowly got out of bed and switched on the bedside lamp. The shapes remained on the wall, and when Frank focused his bleary eyes upon them, he saw the silhouettes of two biplanes engaged in a dogfight. The planes looped the loop and cavorted through the dreary old wallpaper, and during the aerial combat, Frank heard the clattering sound of their machine guns. Moments later, the planes from the era of the Red Baron faded away and a tense silence pervaded the bedroom. What was going on? Frank had the very unsettling feeling of being watched by someone, so he hurriedly grabbed his shirt and trousers and went downstairs.

He had overindulged in drink before, and had never suffered hallucinations as a result. He therefore, irrationally, decided to remove the old wallpaper, which, in his befuddled state, he identified as the root of the problem. Maureen reminded Frank about the 'nightmare' she'd had about the pilot wearing the flying goggles and they both agreed that there was possibly some connection.

There was no more supernatural activity at the house for over a month, then, one afternoon, Maureen's twelve-year-old nephew came to visit. He was standing in the hallway, chatting to his Aunty Maureen, when he suddenly gazed up the stairs at something.

"Who's that?" he asked.

Maureen looked up the stairs, and standing on the landing at the top of the staircase was the very pilot who had confronted her in the bedroom on that unforgettable night. He was standing there in his flying uniform and helmet, smiling down at herself and her nephew. Maureen went numb with shock, and quickly ushered her nephew to the neighbours' house next door, where they both recovered from their ordeal over a cup of tea and a biscuit.

Maureen and Frank decided that enough was enough – they did not care to share their house with a pilot and his aviator friends, and so they moved to a house in Lower Bebington. The identity of the ghostly aviator of Dacre Hill remains unknown.

What makes this case even more unusual is the fact that a ghostly World War One pilot matching the description and behaviour of the Dacre Hill entity used to terrorise a six-year-old girl at her home on Edge Lane in the Kensington area of Liverpool. The ghost used to gesture to her to be quiet by putting his finger to his lips when he appeared in her bedroom. On one occasion the goggled pilot clamped his hand over the terrified girl's mouth, but vanished when she struggled and let out a muffled scream.

Are the ghosts of Dacre Hill and Edge Lane returned pilots from some long-disbanded spectral squadron? Or are the two weird aviators one and the same ghost?

Hooded Harbinger of Death

One cold evening in October, 1974, a nine-year-old girl named Samantha was walking with her ten-year-old friend Joanne down a secluded path at Sherdley Park, near St Helens, when Samantha saw a strange sight. At the end of the lane, directly beneath the thin crescent moon, stood a figure resembling a hooded monk in a long black habit. Samantha pointed the figure out to Joanne, but she couldn't see anything.

Then, without warning, a car came screeching round the bend in the lane up ahead. It swerved violently from side to side as the driver wrestled with the steering wheel to regain control over the car, but his attempt failed and the car slammed into a tree, coming to a dead halt. The noise of the impact was deafening – the shatter of glass; metalwork being twisted and flattened against the tree trunk; tyres bursting and steam escaping from the burst radiator. Instantaneously, as the car concertinered into the tree, a figure came flying headfirst through the front windscreen – just like those dummies in the road safety adverts. In a shower of glass, the figure hit the ground with a dull thump, which forced its head to turn violently and snapped its neck like a twig.

Samantha and Joanne screamed and screamed, overcome with the horror of what they had just witnessed. Meanwhile, the spectral monk, who had watched the accident from the bottom of the lane, hovered across the road towards the crash victim's mangled body, then faded away when it reached him. Only Samantha had been able to see that hooded figure, and long after the trauma of the car crash had faded away, the memory of the sinister ghost remained – vivid and all too real – and often featured in many of her nightmares. Her mother and father tried to soothe their daughter by telling her that the monk had been nothing more than a trick of the light, but Samantha knew better, and she was to encounter what appeared to have been some type of Grim Reaper again, on one further occasion.

In 1979, Samantha was a fourteen-year-old living with her family in the Croxteth area of Liverpool, and on the Monday evening of 5 November of that year – Guy Fawkes Night – she was looking forward to going to a friend's house on Carr Lane, for a bonfire night party.

As she set off, she took a deep breath, which further fuelled her excitement; the air was filled with sulphurous fumes and the skies alive with coloured flares and rockets. There was also a full moon looming over Croxteth on the eastern horizon, which brought everything into sharp focus. Samantha couldn't wait to get to the firework display that her friend's parents would be putting on in their back garden, and so she strode down Stonebridge Lane with an enthusiastic spring in her step. All her eager anticipation instantly drained away, however, when she suddenly came upon the black monk again.

A hackney cab had just pulled up outside a terraced house, and two women, aged about seventy something, alighted from the vehicle and walked up the path towards the house. They were completely oblivious to the eerie black figure who suddenly sped towards them out of nowhere. Samantha froze in her tracks as she watched the supernatural entity that was just thirty yards away. From this distance she could see that, instead of a living person, there was a skull beneath the hood, and its hands and feet were also skeletal. Not only was the monk's appearance alarming, but the behaviour of this spine-chilling figure – which again, could apparently only be seen by Samantha – was also decidedly odd and unnerving.

The mad monk danced around the two pensioners as they walked along, then dashed ahead of them and started to stamp its bony foot on their front door step. The figure then vanished, as one of the two women opened the door with a key. By this time, they had both noticed Samantha, who was staring at them open-mouthed near their front gate. The women stood in the hallway, watching the teenaged girl, suspecting that she was up to no good. Samantha pulled herself together and hurried off down the dark lane to her friend's house. She started to tell her friend and her friend's parents what she had seen, but they obviously didn't believe her, so she gave up.

A few days later, Samantha was walking up the same road where she had seen the dancing skeleton on bonfire night – when she saw something that made her stomach churn. There was a woman carrying funeral wreaths from a car into the house where the two elderly ladies lived. Had one of them died? And was the monk-like figure some kind of angel of death?

Samantha was telling her friend in Carr Lane what she had just seen, when the girl's parents overheard her. They told Samantha that not just one, but both old women who had lived in the house in question had died within minutes of one another in mysterious circumstances. They had been sisters, and apparently, one of them had died from hypothermia, and the other had then suffered a stroke – probably when she came across her sister lying dead on the floor of the hallway. It was a terrible double tragedy which had shocked and saddened the whole neighbourhood.

To this day, Samantha still lives in fear of another meeting with the weird harbinger of death.

A Dance with Death

In the summer of 1885, a small slender woman with a pale childish face visited Liverpool. She was twenty-nine-year-old Elizabeth Berry of Oldham, and she had come to the city to visit a relative who lived on Duke Street.

After the visit, Elizabeth journeyed across the Mersey on the ferry to see a cousin over at New Brighton, and ended up staying at the seaside resort for three days. On the last day of her visit, Elizabeth entered the tent of the expensive and controversial fortune-teller, Madame Rosamund, who had intrigued her since the day she arrived. Rosamund, who claimed to be of Romany descent, broke the golden rule of fortune telling: never reveal the details of a forthcoming death to a client.

"You have had many deaths in your life – Elizabeth," said Rosamund in a strange-sounding low voice, as she peered knowingly into the dark glassy depths of a purple-tinted crystal ball.

"Yes, yes, I have," Elizabeth replied, then queried: "But how do you know my name?"

"Your husband gone … your son gone …" Madame Rosamund whispered.

A shiver of apprehension shot down Elizabeth's spine. What the fortune-teller said was true. Four years ago, Elizabeth's invalid husband, Thomas, had died suddenly, and just over a year later, their son had also passed away. At the time of his death he had been sleeping in a damp bed in Blackpool. Elizabeth had received the sum of seventy pounds from an insurance policy when her husband died, and five pounds for the death of her son.

"Oh! The shadow is reaching out now for your daughter …" said Rosamund enigmatically, looking at her terrified client from under her jet black lashes.

Rosamund's large dark eyes widened and probed deeper into the very nucleus of the crystal sphere. Elizabeth felt faint at the shocking news, but there was another terrible revelation still to come. Oblivious to Elizabeth's evident distress, Rosamund continued to reel off what lay in store for the young widow in the future.

"You will dance with a tall dark stranger, and he will drop you and take your life. His eyes are brown – they twinkle like the stars – and he will captivate you, but he will surely kill you. His eyes will be full of tears when he sees what he has done. You will then go to the terrible place of darkness and gnashing of teeth."

Trembling, Elizabeth stood up, and backed away from the sinister fortune teller. The unrepentant Madame Rosamund covered the crystal ball with a dark green velvet cloth and gently shook her head, "I only read the future, my dear, warts and all."

Some time later, Elizabeth was invited to a ball in Oldham by her local butcher, thirty-five-year-old Tom Whittaker. Elizabeth politely declined the invitation, concerned lest Whittaker should turn out to be the tall dark man with the twinkling brown eyes who would kill her. He was certainly tall and dark-eyed, and Elizabeth had often winced at the way the young butcher would hack the blood-drained carcasses with his enormous meat cleaver. She shuddered at the recollection. No! She would rather stay at home with her knitting, thank you very much!

A month after that, old Mr Hargreaves, the counter clerk from the local post office, invited the pretty young widow to a soirée at the local church hall. Mr Hargreaves was bald and blue-eyed, so there was no way he could be the brown-eyed killer foretold by the fortune-teller, and she accepted his invitation, thinking it would make a pleasant, if rather unexciting, change.

So Elizabeth Berry walked hand in hand with a man old enough to be her father into a church hall one hot July night in 1885. The two of them joined in the dancing, until, at one point in the evening, Mr Hargreaves sat down to rest his weary legs, leaving Elizabeth on the periphery of the dance floor, still eager to join in the dancing. She made a very pretty picture, with her black curly hair tied up with a silk crimson bow, and her ivory white dress prettily adorned with pearls and pink roses. Her round face was childish, and being powdered and flushed from all the dancing, she didn't look a day over sixteen.

She did not have to wait long before a tall man with hair as black and curly as Elizabeth's own approached her. He invited her to dance, but she shook her head and cast her eyes down, nervously.

Death had arrived.

"Oh, come now, don't be such a wallflower," teased the man in a deep voice, betraying an American accent.

Without waiting for a reply, the tall dark stranger grabbed her hand and Elizabeth felt dizzy and faint. She almost fell towards him. Her heart was palpitating. She was a helpless doll in his muscular arms, and he waltzed wildly with her across the dance floor. Everything was swirling. The chandelier swam by overhead, and the other couples spun past like mad dervishes. The American's cologne was masculine and as overpowering as he himself was. The heady aroma stifled her, yet Elizabeth Berry had never felt more alive in all of her twenty-nine years.

When the musicians stopped playing and the waltz ended, Elizabeth and the American were out of breath, and both were obviously filled with lust for one another. Growing increasingly agitated, Mr Hargreaves had been watching all these goings on from the sidelines and at the earliest opportunity he grabbed Elizabeth's arm, upon which the American, a Texan whose name was Brett, said, "Sir, may I compliment you? Your daughter is truly the finest English Rose I have set eyes upon since coming to this country."

Hargreaves ample cheeks puffed with fury, and in no uncertain terms, he told Brett that he was not Elizabeth's father, but a good friend. Two other men who had been eyeing Elizabeth Berry with lecherous desire, seized their opportunity and they confronted the American and accused him of insulting a senior citizen of Oldham. A serious fight ensued, and Hargreaves and another man bundled Elizabeth Berry out of the church hall and took her home. At her gate, Hargreaves made a pass at Elizabeth, but she laughingly told him that she was not interested in him in a physical way, merely as a friend. When Hargreaves heard the bare, unpalatable truth, he surprised her by bursting into tears, then sucking his thumb!

That night, Elizabeth lay awake in her bed, thinking constantly of Brett's wide manly shoulders, his sleek black hair, and those dark penetrating brown eyes. She was so totally smitten that she convinced herself that Madame Rosamund had lied to her – the handsome American couldn't possibly do her any harm.

The summer mellowed as the weeks passed, and in the late August of 1885, a young local policeman named Bob Oakley invited Elizabeth to another ball, this time in Manchester. The ball had been organised by the Manchester Police Force, and most of the people attending the occasion were either policemen, ex-policemen, or their relatives. Young Oakley never danced once with Elizabeth Berry, as he didn't get a chance. She had created quite a stir, and the hot-blooded police constables crowded about her and queued up to take her in their arms and sweep her across the dance floor.

Of all the men who waylaid her that evening, only one caught the eye and heart of Elizabeth, and his name was James. He was tall, with hair as black as coal, and eyes of smouldering lignite brown. They flashed with emotion as James twirled her effortlessly around the dance floor. Elizabeth sat at a table with James and found him to be the most perfect, courteous, gallant and handsome man she had ever set eyes upon. She told him about her bereavements, and how she hoped to rebuild a life for herself and her daughter and become a nurse at the Oldham Workhouse, but when Elizabeth tried to discover if James was a policeman, he steered the conversation away in another direction. All Elizabeth was able to ascertain from the conversation was that James was a bachelor. Anyway, whatever his occupation, she argued to herself, he was obviously a kind and caring man. Yet again, although James matched perfectly Rosamund's description of Elizabeth's future killer, her emotions were powerful enough to blot out the fortune teller's awful predictions.

Then came a most curious coincidence. James learned that Elizabeth's surname was the same as his – Berry. If they married, James mused, Elizabeth would still retain her original surname. All this talk of marriage gave Elizabeth the courage to hint that perhaps they should keep in touch, but James Berry sighed and told her that his work would be taking him to another town, faraway, in the morning. After that, he was needed in another part of the country, and such was the itinerant nature of his job, that he was rarely in one place for more than a day at a time.

That night, James guided Elizabeth out on to a balcony, as every other couple savoured the last waltz. They clung to each other and kissed passionately by the light of the full moon, as the last strains of the music filled their ears. James said he knew in his soul that he would meet Elizabeth again one day, and when that day came, he would give up his work and marry her. They both cried on the balcony beneath the moon and stars. But, within half an hour, James was travelling east, and Elizabeth was travelling west back to Oldham.

Elizabeth Berry worked for a while as a nurse at the OldhamWorkhouse, but she did not really enjoy the work, and inwardly believed that she deserved a better station in life. Her annual salary was just twenty-five pounds, and that was not nearly enough to pay for good clothes and a decent lifestyle. Elizabeth had a strange dual personality, and she would be kindness itself to the patients one day, and cruel and heartless to them the next. There were also strange rumours circulating about the daughter Elizabeth Berry hardly mentioned. This was eleven-year-old Edith Annie Berry, whom she had placed in the care of an aunt.

In January 1887, Elizabeth invited the child back into her life, but unfortunately, the girl fell gravely ill within days of the reunion. Elizabeth Berry's neighbours, who had no doubt already decided that she was a bit of a flighty piece, because of all her admirers, whispered that the widow was cursed, but others attributed Edith Annie's illness to a rather more sinister cause. After all, it was widely known that Edith's mother had recently taken out an insurance policy on her daughter, and stood to receive ten pounds compensation if the girl should die. This was true – however, Elizabeth Berry had also taken out a second policy that would pay out one hundred pounds to either Edith or her mother, depending on who lived the longer.

Little Edith Annie died in agony at five o'clock in the morning on the day after she had fallen ill. Given that Elizabeth Berry had now lost a husband, a son and a daughter to mysterious illnesses, and had received insurance payouts in each case, foul play was suspected. A Dr Patterson and several other doctors performed a post-mortem on Edith Annie – and discovered a powerful poison – possibly sulphuric acid – both in her stomach and in samples of her vomit.

Several people who had known Elizabeth came forward and expressed their belief that she had even murdered her own mother with poison, as she had died in similar circumstances. So Elizabeth's mother was duly exhumed – and poison was indeed found in her stomach. Other former friends added to the case for the prosecution, claiming that Elizabeth not only smoked opium, but was an immoral flirt who read sensational lurid novels. All Elizabeth Berry could say in her defence was that if, as the prosecution claimed, she had poisoned her mother, husband and children, then she must have been insane at the time.

However, her pleas of insanity went unheeded and she was tried, found guilty and sentenced to death for the murder of her mother by poisoning. A second case – that she had murdered Edith Annie – was not brought before the courts. The date set for her execution was Monday, 14 March 1887, and the place was Kirkdale Prison.

That fateful day soon arrived, and hundreds of Liverpudlians who had eagerly read the lurid accounts of the dreadful poisonings, braved the snow and icy winds as they gathered at the foot of the prison walls. Immediately prior to the execution, the hangman visited Elizabeth in her cell. She looked up as he entered and realised at once that it was James Berry, the man she had danced with two years before. When they saw one another, they stood motionless, both of them in shock. The prison warders glanced back and forth between Elizabeth and James, until one of them said, "Have you met before?"

James Berry nodded, and asked if he could spend a few private moments alone with the condemned woman.

"Of course," said the senior warder. "Knock when you want us to collect her."

The hangman and the murderess embraced in the cold dark cell, and both faintly sobbed. Madame Rosamund's prophecy had come to pass ... You will dance with a tall dark stranger, and he will drop you and take your life. His eyes are brown, they twinkle like the stars, and he will captivate you, but he will surely kill you. His eyes will be full of tears when he sees what he has done ...

James assured Elizabeth that her death would be quick and painless. He would make sure of that in the positioning of the knot around her beautiful, delicate neck.

Outside in the prison yard, warders were sprinkling sand over the snowy path to the gallows, to make sure that Elizabeth would not slip. Meanwhile, in the cell, the hangman was saying, "I never forgot you in those two years, Elizabeth. No woman has eyes as beautiful as yours. No woman on this earth has touched my heart the way that you did that moonlit summer night."

The hands of the prison clock ticked relentlessly on, and soon the warders grew impatient. They knocked on the cell door and asked James Berry if he was ready. In a choked voice, he replied that he was. The chaplain accompanied Elizabeth and the warders and the executioner to the gallows. James Berry climbed up first and readied himself for the dreadful task that lay ahead. He glanced down and saw that Elizabeth had fainted. Two warders carried her up to the scaffold, and she was positioned over the trapdoor – or 'the drop', as it was known.

As James Berry pinioned her feet together and adjusted the straps, Elizabeth regained consciousness, and gasped in horror as the heavy noose was adjusted around her neck.

"May the Lord have mercy upon me," she whispered. "Lord receive my spirit."

The white hood was gently placed over her head, and she kissed the hangman's hand as he pulled the cloth over her soft face. The chaplain prayed in a low muttering voice, and James Berry closed his eyes as he threw the lever which drew the bolt. In an instant, the trapdoor sprang open and Elizabeth Berry plunged into eternity.

James Berry would later voluntarily retire from his grisly occupation and openly condemned capital punishment as an obscene abomination. People often asked him why he had abandoned and attacked his own profession in such a way, and Berry would always refuse to give a satisfactory explanation, but I'm sure that Elizabeth's death was the sole reason.

Without You

In the Garston area of Liverpool, in September 1974, twenty-two-year-old Beth moved into a two-bedroom house with her two-year-old daughter. Her partner Jeff had recently deserted her, and Beth's friends, most of whom she had known since her schooldays, often visited her and encouraged her to go out.

The house was small but cosy and Beth had been looking forward to living in it. However, from the very first day that she moved in, she immediately sensed the faint presence of a previous female resident. Beth was not in the least bit psychic, but she couldn't shake off the feeling. Perhaps it was the aroma of Mansion House furniture polish in the hall, or the strong scent of lavender which greeted her nose in the living room. Beth had no washing machine or tumble dryer when she moved in, and she hadn't really been prepared for living on her own. She looked at the pile of baby's washing and sighed, then some strange instinct guided her to a cupboard in the kitchen, where she found a large tin box crammed with clothing pegs, wire wool, a length of clothes line, candles, dusters and other knick-knacks. Next to the box there were several old but half-full and still usable boxes of Omo washing powder, a can of Brasso metal polish, and a tube of Ajax bleach powder. Beth didn't yet possess a television set either, so she was very grateful for the small transistor radio she found in another of the kitchen cupboards. It looked pretty old, yet it worked perfectly well. Beth tuned into Radio One, her favourite station, listened to a few songs, then switched it off.

Beth's friends brought round food and drink for the house-warming party that she held one Sunday evening, which went on until three in the morning. By two o'clock in the morning, all the girls who had come to the party with their boyfriends had left, but Ruth and Andrea, two of Beth's closest friends, stayed on long after the last guests had gone, helping her to clean up the mess. They then sat around the old open fire, smoking and gossiping. Beth went to put the kettle on the gas stove during their conversation, and as she was filling the kettle, she caught a fleeting glimpse of a woman's face staring back at her through the kitchen window. She shrieked, dropped the kettle into the sink, then ran back into the living room to Ruth and Andrea.

"What's happened? What's the matter – you look like you've seen a ghost," Andrea said. She imagined that Beth had perhaps seen a spider or a mouse, she knew she hated both.

"There's … there's someone in the back garden … some woman," Beth replied.

Ruth went to the window and peeped through the gap in the curtains. Armed with the poker which she had picked up from the grate, Andrea also went into the kitchen. She switched off the kitchen light and peered through the glass panes. She couldn't see any thing unusual, just the starry skies and the barely discernible silhouettes of treetops and the chimneys of the house that backed on to the small garden.

"What was she like?" Ruth asked.

"It was all so fast," said Beth. "She looked really pale, and her eyes were very black, as if she'd been crying. There were streaks running down from them where her mascara had run."

"Wonder what she was doing in your back garden?" Andrea said. "Have you seen her before? Maybe she's a neighbour who's had too much to drink and went into the wrong back garden."

At that moment, the old transistor radio suddenly switched itself on, causing the three women to jump. Earlier, on Sunday evening, Radio 1 had played the Top 30 songs between 5pm and 7pm, then the station had joined Radio 2. No soft-voiced Radio 2 DJ was heard on the radio this time however, just the unnerving sobs of a woman. Moments later, the Harry Nilsson song, *Without You* – which had been at number one a few years before – blared out of the radio at full volume.

Beth picked the radio up and tried to switch it off – but even though she thumbed the volume wheel down until it clicked, the melancholic song continued to play with such intensity, that the radio's speakers vibrated. Ruth took the radio from Beth and located a small removable panel which covered the battery compartment. She removed the panel with the intention of removing the batteries – only to find that there were no batteries in the radio.

As Ruth and Beth looked at one another in puzzlement, the song emanating from the baffling radio finally faded away. There were no further supernatural incidents that night and when dawn came, Ruth and Andrea left. Beth quickly got into bed and buried herself beneath the blankets, unable to get the pale face of the crying woman out of her head. The sobs she had heard on the radio also replayed incessantly in the young woman's mind.

Three days later, Andrea and Ruth both visited Beth's home again at 7pm. Once more they heard the sounds of the same song they'd heard before when the radio had played without a power source. This time the song was not as loud, but still audible enough to be easily recognisable. Beth shuddered, because earlier in the day she had thrown that infernal radio into the dustbin outside. Following the sound of the song, Andrea and Ruth peeped through the doorway into the kitchen, and there was the transistor radio on the draining board adjacent to the sink.

All three women entered the kitchen, and Andrea was the first to dare to pick up the radio. Beth opened the kitchen door that led into the back garden and held her hands out for the radio.

"Give me that thing. It's going back in the bin," she said to Andrea.

The presence of Ruth and Andrea gave her enough confidence to go out into dark garden to dump the radio back in the dustbin. She had no idea how the accursed thing had managed to find its way back into the house, and it was not something she wanted to dwell on. She shoved the radio deep into the refuse, and slammed the lid down with a clang. Whatever is going on, it isn't going to make me live in fear, thought Beth.

Turning back towards the house, she was stopped short by the sight of her two friends standing motionless in the kitchen doorway. Their heads were tilted slightly upwards and their faces were looking at something with expressions of shock and horror. Beth nervously turned and followed the line of their gaze until she found herself looking at a tree at the bottom of the garden. There was something unfamiliar dangling from the black tree branches silhouetted against the ultramarine blue sky of evening; a long black shape that slowly rotated until it presented a pale face. The likeness was unmistakable – it was the very same face that had ever so briefly peeped in at Beth through the kitchen window. Its eyes were large black circles with mascara streaking from them.

Beth screamed and threw her hands up to her face to blot out the image of the hanged woman spiralling gently anti-clockwise, suspended from the second branch of the tree next to the shed, about twelve feet above the ground.

The three women rushed out of the house via the front door and called to two men who were passing by. They told them about the woman hanging in the garden, and the men, seeing how upset they were, followed them into the house and hurried down the hallway. Andrea led them through the kitchen to the back door that was still ajar. The men stepped into the garden and asked where the hanged woman was. Andrea pointed to the tree – and saw that the figure had now vanished. The men scanned the garden, then glanced back at the three women with lightly veiled scepticism. They felt that they had been the subject of some kind of practical joke and soon left, walking quickly down the hallway and back out into the street, ignoring Andrea's assurances that there really had been a woman hanging in the garden.

Understandably, Beth soon decided to move from that Garston house, and many years later, she heard a disturbing story about the place that explained the apparition. Apparently, a twenty-three-year-old woman named Nancy had hanged herself in the garden after her boyfriend had dumped her. At the time of the split, the popular but sad song *Without You* had reached number one in the pop charts, and was constantly played on the radio. The song must have summed up all of the heartbreak which Nancy was experiencing at the time, because the neighbours complained that the inconsolable young woman would turn the radio up to full volume whenever *Without You* was played on air.

Nancy became increasingly depressed and desperate and eventually obtained a length of sturdy rope. It is said that she borrowed it from a neighbour, using the excuse that she needed it to tow a car. The broken-hearted Nancy then climbed up on to the roof of the garden shed and from there to the branch of the tree from which she hanged herself.

Perhaps Nancy is still not at rest, as there have been numerous reports of the frightening, swollen-eyed apparition of her hanging at the house in Garston over the years.

Childhood Bogeyman

I've written before about the pleasant ghosts of childhood, but not about the bogeymen and scary entities which haunted readers in their youth and infancy. Some of us may look back and recall strange supernatural experiences, then try to rationalise them with our dull adult logic, but it would seem that many of the phantasms and fiends of our misty childhood memories were not borne out of imagination at all. Here are a few examples to illustrate my point.

Elize was a beautiful nine-year-old Rainhill girl who had never been in trouble in her short life. She was a girl who loved nothing better than to curl up with an Enid Blyton book or watch the weekly episodes of the television series *Black Beauty* and *Follyfoot*.

One summer evening in 1973, Elize hammered on the front door of her home near Rainhill Stoops, and when her grandmother opened the door, the girl barged in with her clothes torn and her hair in disarray. She was trembling violently and said that a farmer had thrown her off his land. With tears in her eyes, Elize explained that she had been forced to trespass on farm land to get away from a "horrible monster" that had chased her near Cronton Wood.

Elize's grandmother hugged the terrified child and calmed her down somewhat, but Elize kept gibbering almost incoherently, and when her mother and father came into the house from a night out at a restaurant, they were distressed to see the state of their daughter. Elize said that she had been playing hide and seek with her friend Carol in the wood, and when she went off to hide, she saw a purplish light in the distance. This light seemed to expand and contract in a slow hypnotic manner, and when Elize went to see what it was, she was so shocked that she froze. It was the floating head of a woman with black, evil-looking eyes, and more frighteningly, the head had a writhing snake-like mass of tentacles where it's hair should have been. It looked just like the gorgon of Greek mythology. The face was white, but the head was surrounded by an aura of purple light.

Elize turned slowly, and tried to run, but what with the spooky apparition and the irate farmer, her legs had turned to jelly. She gradually regained the ability to run, and when she did, she ran off screaming. She passed her alarmed friend Carol at high speed, and kept on running. She climbed over the fence of a farmer's field and after stumbling into a thorny hedge, she was collared by the farmer who had been inspecting his crops. He assumed she was some kind of juvenile delinquent and threw her off his land without waiting for an explanation. Elize then walked miles to her home, crying and constantly looking behind her to check whether the disembodied head was following her. Elize's parents asked their daughter's friend Carol if she had seen anything in the wood, and the girl said she too had seen a purplish light that moved off into the distance and "went out like a light being switched off".

In the following three months there were several more sightings of the Rainhill gorgon at Sutton Manor, St Anne's Well and Pex Hill, before the terrifying vision finally vanished as mysteriously as it had first appeared.

*

A young lady also features in another intriguing tale that was related to me by her parents. In 1997, six-year-old Georgia told her mother that she couldn't wait to go to bed because her friend Frances had promised that she would come to her that very night. "Who is Frances?" asked Georgia's bewildered mother, Linda.

Georgia explained that Frances was a ghost of a child who used to live in the house "years and years ago" and that she had become a close friend. Linda thought about her daughter's claims for a few moments, but with the mounting chores of housework at hand, she dismissed Frances as a figment of Georgia's imagination.

However, one morning, Georgia was chattering on about her ghostly companion at breakfast, and happened to mention that Frances always had to come out of the wardrobe because the door she came through was behind it. Years before Georgia had been born, when Linda and her husband Tony first moved into the house, they had been stripping the old wallpaper from the rooms, and had discovered that a doorway had once existed in the room now used as their daughter's bedroom. The doorway had led into the room Tony had taken over as an office. All vestiges of that filled-in doorway had long been wallpapered over. Moreover, the old door lay behind the wardrobe, and was completely concealed, so how Georgia knew anything about it was a complete mystery.

The ghost of Frances is alleged to have remained friends with Georgia until she was about ten years old, after which the visitor from some other realm was seen no more. Georgia cried for days and days when Frances left for good, but when she finally got over the loss of her friend, she related some very strange tales about the so-called ghost.

According to Georgia, Frances was the ten-year-old daughter of a Mr and Mrs Blackshaw, and she had a young brother named Jim, who was always ill and bed-bound. Sometimes Georgia and Frances were allowed to push him round the garden in a sort of wheelchair, and it was whispered that the boy did not have long to live. Mrs and Mrs Blackshaw often told Georgia that she didn't belong in their "day and age" and would then escort her to a door that took her back to her bedroom and the present day.

Apparently, there was also a frightening man in black who wore a top hat and a long cape who used to come into Georgia's room via the wardrobe mirror. He had once introduced himself as Barnabas and had proceeded to kiss her and try to pull her from her bed. His breath smelt foul and whenever the protesting Georgia let out a scream of revulsion, Barnabas would flee through the wardrobe mirror, and then peep out from it to check if the girl's parents had come to her aid. When Georgia told Frances about Barnabas, she explained that he was her mad uncle.

All this could, of course, be explained away as a product of Georgia's imaginative mind, but what Linda and Tony couldn't explain was how she was able to provide intriguing details from what she described as her "other life" in Victorian times. She was able to talk about and describe in detail the farthings, florins and sovereigns which made up the Victorian currency, and used many outdated phrases and sayings from that era that would only be known to an historian, or reader of Victorian literature.

I have carried out my own researches on the house where Frances allegedly took Georgia through a long vanished doorway into the past, and have ascertained that the Blackshaw family did indeed live there. What's more, they also had a daughter whose name was Frances, but I cannot find any traces of her young brother, or of the sinister Uncle Barnabas.

*

Tom Walker now lives in Australia, but when he was a child growing up in Bebington, he lived in mortal fear of a weird and extremely agile ghost that haunted Bebington Mill in the early 1960s. The cone-shaped tower of the mill seemed deserted to Tom, but things were often seen to be moving behind the black squares of the rotted window frames on each of the building's three storeys. Tom often roamed around the area surrounding the mill in the company of a small gang of friends whose leader was a wild fourteen-year-old named Jack, whose main hobby seemed to be causing as much disruption as possible for the citizens of Bebington.

One summer night, Jack noticed a figure peering out from the top empty window frame of Bebington Mill, and he drew the gang's attention to the person. Tom was wary and warned him that he had heard the mill was haunted, but Jack took no notice and shouted up to the thing peering out through the dilapidated window, "Hey, you! Are you spying on us? We'll come up and throw you out the window, mate!"

The gang of five laughed nervously as the figure moved away from the window ledge into the dark interior of the mill, only to reappear in a window on the next floor some moments later, this time waving his fist. He seemed to have a head of long white hair.

"Let's go, Jack," said Tom Walker, his voice betraying a deep sense of unease.

"He's just some old tramp," Jack declared, with his usual swagger. "We'll give him a good kicking."

The gang members waited to see what their leader would do next. Jack looked about him and was just about to pick up a three-foot length of wood, when a man with long white hair, dressed in a bib and brace, and wielding a long-handled axe, came charging towards the gang from the direction of the mill. Jack swore loudly and ran off, leaving the gang to scatter in all directions.

Tom pushed one of the boys out of the way as he made his escape, and witnessed the terrifying sight of the axe flying past him. Fortunately, it landed in the hedge to his right without hitting any of the fleeing youngsters. The man continued to pursue the boys and let out a string of shocking expletives and obscene insults. Tom managed to glance back once and saw the white-haired madman running along like a gazelle, even though he appeared to be around sixty years of age at least.

Jack must have possessed amazing powers of persuasion, because he managed to coax them all back to the old mill the very next evening, and once again he started to taunt the elderly axe-man. On this occasion, the gang members scattered as soon as the old man appeared, but Jack fell over in the retreat, and was to receive the shock of his life. The sprightly old man quickly caught up with him and proceeded to kick him in the stomach, but, thankfully, after the third kick, the attacker vanished right before his eyes.

Many years later, when Tom Walker was an adult, he bumped into his old friend Jack on a cruise ship, and the two men reminisced about their childhood adventures. When Tom mentioned the ghost of Bebington Mill, Jack's face went pale, and he said, "For years I told myself that I had imagined that old man."

"You didn't imagine him, Jack," Tom told him. "He was as real as you or me."

The identity of the white-haired ghost remains a mystery.

*

Finally, in April 2004, I received a letter from Selina in Croxteth about another childhood ghost:

When I was eleven years old, I was sitting in my bedroom one evening, watching television, when my dad shouted to me from his bedroom, asking for a glass of milk, as he suffered from stomach ulcers. So off I went to fetch the milk, and on my way back, as I was halfway up the stairs, I saw what I thought was my three-year-old sister walking along the landing into my bedroom. I shouted for her to come out of my room in case she broke something. I then experienced a strange urge to look into my sister's bedroom, and to my astonishment, I saw that she was actually tucked up in bed sound asleep.

I then took the milk up to my parents' room and told them about the little girl who had just walked into my bedroom, and how I had mistaken her for my sister. Mum and Dad looked at each other with nervous expressions. Dad asked me what the little girl looked like, and I told him that she seemed to be around three years of age, with blonde hair, and she had worn a long white nightdress. Dad raised an eyebrow and told me I was seeing things because I was tired, but I wasn't tired at all.

That night I couldn't sleep because of the fear of seeing a ghost on the landing going into my room, and I left the light on and hid my head under the sheets.

In time I forgot all about the ghost, and four years passed by. Then, at the age of fifteen, I once again saw the little blonde girl in the white nightdress walking along the landing and into my bedroom, and I was even more scared than the last time I had seen her. She walked straight past me as if I wasn't there. I turned and ran down the stairs as fast my legs would carry me – straight into the living room where my Mum was sitting reading the paper.

"Are you alright, love? You look a bit pale," Mum commented, and I told her what I had just seen.

She told me that when she and dad first moved into the house, when I was a one-year-

old child, she was awakened by a little child in the bedroom one night. She thought it was me, and when she got up she went into my bedroom, only to find that I was fast asleep. My Mum woke Dad up and told him about the weird incident, and made him stay awake with her all night. Dad said he didn't believe in ghosts until one night, later that week, when he was awakened by a sharp slap across the face. He woke up, startled, to find a little blonde girl standing at his bedside, smiling up at him. He called to Mum, and she woke up and also saw the ghostly child. She had never seen my father in such a state before – he was terrified.

The girl later vanished, and hasn't been seen since. I am now twenty years old and I'm still sleeping in the same bedroom.

The Cupid's Bow Murder

Up in the northern extremities of Northumberland, at a place called Wooler, on the Scottish border, there are a series of ancient markings which were engraved on sandstone boulders over three thousand years ago. Their meaning continues to baffle archaeologists. The markings are unique in the British Isles, and they include a group of concave spherical shapes, each around ten inches in diameter, whilst another is the carving of an adult footprint. Among the mysterious carvings there is an arrow and a heart, hewn out of the stone, and this strikes me as a rather black coincidence, because nearby, in the 1870s, the mystifying Cupid's Bow murder took place, and the man suspected of carrying out the ultimate crime of passion came from Liverpool.

In 1875, fifty-year-old widower James Thorpe of Little Bongs, Knotty Ash, inherited a vast fortune, left to him by his spinster aunt. Rather than investing his newfound wealth, he chose instead to travel the world.

In Sicily, in 1876, he met a young woman who was to change the course of his life. Her name was Rosalia Salvatore, a small, shapely attractive eighteen-year-old. Thorpe fell instantly in love with the brown-eyed beauty and, in a rather shameful transaction, bought her from her father. The girl was brought to England, and Thorpe was soon showing her off at every soirée and dance. However, Rosalia was so beautiful, that when she graced the dance floor, the men only noticed her and not her middle-aged, nondescript partner – it was as if Thorpe had become invisible in her presence, such was his fiancée's stunning Latin beauty. All the women, on the other hand, instantly hated the poor girl because their husbands and fiancés were mesmerised by her good looks.

A steady stream of vitriolic green-inked hate letters were sent from anonymous women to Thorpe's mansion, criticising both his and his young 'foreign' fiancée's behaviour. Thorpe endured the hate mail for months before deciding to purchase a cottage in Northumberland, near Doddington Moor, where he and Rosalia could take refuge from the green-eyed women of Liverpool's high society.

At Rothbury Cottage, James and Rosalia enjoyed the secluded rural life. They walked hand in hand over the rugged heather moorland, enjoyed the birdsong which filled the coniferous forests, and pondered their love amid the prehistoric crags and ancient megalithic standing stones which dotted the area.

However, in the summer of 1877, the eternal love triangle reared its ugly head when Jem Garnock, a huge giant of a man, visited Rothbury Cottage. James Thorpe's twenty-five-year-old cousin called out of the blue, asking for employment. He'd recently fallen on hard times after losing his job as a printer's overseer because of an altercation. Broad-shouldered Jem stood at six feet and three inches high in his stocking feet, and with his long flowing black hair and walrus moustache, he was of striking appearance. The moment he set eyes on the delightful Rosalia, he fell for her, and his physical ruggedness and youth likewise instantly captivated her.

James Thorpe was no blind fool, and he quickly noticed the way his wife-to-be was eyeing his cousin, so he told Jem to return to Liverpool at once, and accused him of being a freeloading loafer. In broken English, Rosalia interposed and begged her husband to at least feed Jem before sending him on his way. Jem enjoyed a hearty meal thanks to her, but before he had time to digest it, he was shown the door.

However, it seems that Jem did not return to Liverpool that night. Instead he obtained work with a team of woodcutters in the forests of the Cheviot Hills. Jem visited Rosalia in secret several times, and James soon became very suspicious when the girl asked to be alone when she embarked on her early evening strolls.

On the morning of Midsummer's Day, a ghostly mist rolled in from the North Sea and swirled over Doddington Moor and Rothbury Cottage. James Thorpe awoke to find Rosalia Salvatore absent from his bed. He looked out of the window into the thick mist, and saw a spectral figure hurrying away in the distance.

Around seven o'clock that morning, Jem Garnock gently embraced Rosalia beneath the sprawling branches of a large lime tree. He started to kiss her passionately, and as he did so, he pushed her against the tree trunk. The beauty from Persephone's island gazed into Jem's slate-grey eyes and sighed, "I love you, ti amato …"

Her words of love were instantly cut short in the most brutal fashion. Something slammed hard and deep with a thud into Jem's back. The impact crushed his body against Rosalia, and she yelped in pain. Reflexively, he tried to pull away – but found himself pinned to her somehow. His back and chest felt numb. Rosalia's mouth opened wide, and blood began to trickle from the side of her lip. She gazed up at him with her stunningly beautiful eyes, but the twinkle had gone from them. They rolled upwards as the lids closed. Her head slumped forward, and came to rest on Jem's chest.

He gently lifted her head and looked down. He saw blood on his waistcoat, and a bright red bloodstain blossoming on the front of Rosalia's blouse. He felt the warm blood from both their wounds trickle down through his clothes. Something had impaled him and his forbidden love to the trunk of the lime tree. Jem cried out in agony as he desperately tried to feel what the thing was that had gone right through his chest and then through Rosalia's heart.

He managed to pull the dead girl from the tree, and felt her back. The sharp tip of an arrow protruded from it. Carrying his beloved's body, he staggered a few feet, then fell. Their bodies remained skewered together by the arrow. The mists around him seemed to darken and soon afterwards, Jem Garnock lost consciousness. He awoke some time later to find himself in a cottage, with a policeman and a doctor at his side. The doctor told him that the arrow had narrowly missed his heart, but had grazed one of his lungs. It had been a chance in a million. Unfortunately, the arrow had passed straight through him and had continued through the lady's heart.

A detective was soon at the cottage. In the course of his speculations he wondered if a stray arrow shot by someone out hunting game had been the cause of the tragedy, but Jem was quick to refute this supposition and accuse his cousin, James Thorpe. An indignant James, when questioned, told the detective that he had slept until almost eight o'clock that morning, and was suffering from heart trouble because of the shock of losing his fiancée in such a shocking way. He added that if his cousin hadn't been recovering from the arrow wound, he would have horse whipped him for courting Rosalia behind his back. The detective then asked Thorpe if he had ever used a bow and arrow, and the Liverpool businessman screamed back a vehement denial. Thorpe said that he agreed with the detective's initial theory, believing that a hunter had accidentally killed his fiancée and was probably too terrified to come forward.

Rosalia was buried in a local churchyard, and James Thorpe eventually returned to Liverpool, where several people, on hearing the circumstances of his fiancée's death, recalled that he had taken part in several archery competitions at Sefton Park five years previously. Meanwhile, Thorpe had confided to his closest friends that he was convinced that the Camorra, the secret criminal organisation in Rosalia's country, had been behind the killing and wounding. However, a man who had travelled extensively around Sicily and Italy said that the Camorra would never have killed a woman; it was taboo to do so, and completely unthinkable. Having heard this, Thorpe then suggested that perhaps they had really intended to kill his cousin and had accidentally killed Rosalia in the process.

"Then why not simply use a dagger?" asked Thorpe's friend. "That's how the Camorra usually kill. They believe in facing the victim as they kill, it's all part of their code."

James Thorpe had no answer for this and realised that he was fooling no one, and therefore decided to hide himself away. Rumours and theories about his guilt abounded, but it seems that for the remainder of his life, James Thorpe was repeatedly haunted by the ghost of Rosalia in a most sinister and terrifying way.

The first supernatural incident in these series of hauntings was witnessed by Thorpe, his butler, and a maidservant at his home near Stanley Park on 21 June 1878 – the first anniversary of Rosalia's untimely death. The mantelpiece clock in the drawing room on the first floor was striking nine in the evening, and Thorpe was relaxing in his soft, leather-padded Wolsey chair, when he heard a faint crashing sound coming from somewhere in the house. At first he thought it sounded like the cook dropping some dinner plates, but then he heard the screams of the young maidservant in the back parlour. Thorpe rushed out of the drawing room and looked down the stairs towards the hall, where he saw the elderly butler emerging from the back parlour, trembling and confused.

"What's the matter?" Thorpe shouted down to the servant, as he hurried down the stairs.

By way of reply, the old butler made an incoherent gibbering sound, and turned to push the parlour door open. What James Thorpe saw in that room sent an icy tingle down his spine. An arrow had been shot into his large oil portrait hanging on the wall. Splinters and fragments from the shattered windowpane were scattered all over the floor near to the window, where the arrow had smashed its way into the room.

The maid suddenly emerged from a dark corner of the parlour and peeped over the chiffonier at Thorpe. She tried to speak but was as unintelligible as the butler. After a stiff drink, the pair of servants eventually managed to relate a very eerie account of their experiences.

Apparently, they had seen what looked like a woman in a long white gown floating past the window. In her hand she held a longbow and an arrow, which she aimed very deliberately at the windows. She fired the arrow straight through the window, then floated off into the evening sky, towards the park. James Thorpe shuddered, particularly when he realised that his fiancée had died exactly one year before. He suspected Jem Garnock of staging the 'ghost hoax' but when he made enquiries about him, he was reliably informed that he had emigrated to America.

Further incidents followed, terrorising the entire household. In the end the ghostly activities became so intense that the butler and five other servants decided to pack up and leave the house. It is said that a policeman also witnessed the ghostly female archer in the shroud, floating over the walls surrounding Thorpe's mansion in the moonlight.

James Thorpe was forced to move yet again and went to live in Ireland, and people said that he was even persecuted there by the ghost of a shroud-clad woman. Thorpe became a convert to Roman Catholicism soon afterwards and died in London in 1900, aged seventy-five.

The Pyromaniac

The following strange tale was investigated by a reporter from the *London Daily Chronicle* in Victorian times. It concerned an eerie self-made man who worshipped a god of fire and practised Occultism.

On the balmy Tuesday evening of 9 August 1898, a fire of mysterious origin engulfed a boarding house in St Paul's Square, off Bixteth Street in Liverpool. Four foreign sailors perished in the blaze, and as their harrowing screams were echoing about the square that night, a tall, top-hatted gentleman in a cape stood nearby accompanied by a gaggle of ragged clothed street urchins.

The caped man and his little helpers stood in a corner of the square as the local people rushed frantically back and forth with pails of water, in an effort to extinguish the blaze. The screams died away quite suddenly and then red tongues of fire spread uniformly out of the heat busted window frames and seared the guttering. In the midst of all this turmoil surrounding the tragic inferno, a policeman noticed the elderly top-hatted gentleman lurking in the dark corner, and then recognised him. Although the policeman had served many years in the Liverpool constabulary, and had witnessed many frightening and distressing sights, he experienced a shudder of revulsion when he spotted Henry Juvenal, because he had seen the same distinguished but sinister gentleman on two previous occasions – on both of which he had been watching a blaze. The officer of the law watched in disgust as Juvenal smiled with satisfaction and closed his eyes, as he tilted back his head slightly, savouring the inhalation of smoke.

At that moment, the clanging bell of the horse-drawn fire engine suddenly distracted the constable as it careered into the square. Half an hour later, the well-to-do but decidedly weird pyromaniac and his gaggle of grubby barefoot children had gone.

Just over a fortnight later, Henry Juvenal was spotted once again standing amid a street gang of impoverished children in the vicinity of a large fire. On this occasion, a zoo was ablaze. Cross's Menagerie in the city was going up in smoke and the wild animals were squealing and howling as the flames roasted them alive. This time, Juvenal and his entourage of sooty-faced juveniles were moved on by the police and members of the fire brigade. One fireman, who was tired of seeing Henry Juvenal at the scene of every fire he attended, voiced out loud what everyone was thinking; that it was suspicious how Juvenal was always to be found in close proximity to a major fire – as if he had started it himself perhaps.

Enraged that he was to be denied his perverse pleasure on this occasion, the arrogant Juvenal swung his walking cane in rage at one of the fireman, narrowly missing his helmet. A policeman, assisted by a member of the public, pushed Juvenal away from the fireman and his colleagues, but the gang of children swarmed around those apprehending the eccentric old man and clung on to their clothes. The policeman blew his whistle and the children scattered. Juvenal backed away and swore he would take legal action against the fireman for defamation of character.

The bizarre tales concerning Henry Juvenal travelled far and wide and soon reached the ears of Alfred Robinson, a reporter for the *London Daily Chronicle*. Robinson journeyed to Liverpool and set about gathering information about the mysterious Juvenal. He discovered that he had been present when Crosby Lighthouse had been destroyed by a mystifying fire on 2 February of that year. The fire had claimed three people's lives, including the lighthouse keeper and his wife. In the course of his investigations, the reporter visited the inhabitants of St Paul's Square, where the four seamen had died in the lodging house blaze. A few of the square's residents recalled having seen the old man with the top hat, cape and walking cane, strolling suspiciously round the square after dark, chatting to the street children, and giving some of them money.

It was time for Robinson to call upon the enigmatic Henry Juvenal in person, and coincidentally, the day the reporter decided to go in search of the fire-obsessed old man happened to be Guy Fawkes night. There seemed to be no record of Juvenal's address in any directory, but it was generally known that his home was a distinctive red brick house on the eastern extremities of Edge Lane, somewhere between Broadgreen and Bowring Park.

Robinson finally located the grand dwelling of Henry Juvenal as night was falling. A ground mist oozed through the high, wrought iron rails of the front gates. At the top of each gatepost was the horned head of a gargoyle, and carved into the stonework of these posts, in bas-relief, were various figures of myth associated with fire, including the phoenix arising from the flames, and the fire-resistant salamander.

The gates were not locked, so Alfred Robinson was able to enter the elegant grounds of the grandiose house and he walked with some apprehension up the long curved path towards the front door. A huge black dog trotted out of the gloom and mist and growled menacingly at the reporter, exposing its sharp, yellow fangs. Robinson froze at the sight of the massive beast. The coal-black Newfoundland Labrador stopped less than six feet away from him and seemed ready to pounce, when Robinson suddenly became aware of an orange and yellow luminescence which flared up from the depths of the ground fog.

A shrill whistle was heard, and the dog's ears immediately pricked up. It then turned and loped back into the dark grey limbo of the evening vapours. Then came a row of fiery lights – a weird, torch-lit procession of some sort. The torches were heading his way, and all Robinson's instincts told him to flee, but he was a professional reporter, and decided to stand his ground; knowing from experience that it was the only way to get the facts of a story. Cowering in the bushes, or running away would not do for the *Chronicle*. Robinson feared his editor more than the strange situation at hand.

Then Henry Juvenal himself approached, carrying a sputtering flaming torch aloft and wearing a pointed hat and flowing robes like the Grand Wizard of the Ku Klux Klan. Surrounding him were five boys, also wearing pointed hats, and each carrying lit torches like their adult leader.

"Sir, you are trespassing!" bawled Juvenal, "What is your business here?"

"Are you Henry Juvenal?" asked Robinson, and he caught a quick glimpse of the black dog's eyes, ominously reflecting the torchlight.

"I am, and what is it to you?" asked Juvenal imperiously, as he squinted at the reporter.

"Sir, you are a most difficult man to contact. I have come from the *Daily Chronicle* in London to write an article about you," Robinson told him, fully expecting to be attacked at any minute.

Instead, the deeply etched features of Juvenal's face softened, and he seemed bemused and even flattered. The reporter was invited to the bonfire party which Juvenal and the children had set up on the land at the back of the house. Robinson assumed that the bonfire party was to be a normal Guy Fawkes one, but when he turned the corner, he saw something very sinister; towering above him was a stone idol, and something was kicking and wriggling in its arms. Trying to remain calm, Robinson talked rather incoherently about the rumours and allegations of arson surrounding Juvenal, as he followed the old man and his little disciples towards the idol.

'Sir, may I ask you what this is?" he enquired, and produced a small notebook and pencil with which he set about describing the statue in shorthand.

The deity was about eighteen feet in height, and looked as if it was made of basalt. It had the head of a horned bull, and the fearsome face of a devil with a mouth full of large fangs. Two arms that stretched out from the statue held a live sheep. The animal was bound to the stone claws of the idol, and seemed almost snug as it nestled against several holes in the statue's chest. These holes led down into a hollowed-out section at the base of the strange idol which was crammed with kindling and firewood.

"This is my idol of Moloch, an underrated god of the ancients. They burned babies on replicas of this statue long ago," said Juvenal matter-of-factly, "but the damned authorities make it hard to do that today."

Alfred Robinson's blood ran cold. He did his best to try and talk Juvenal and the children out of the cruel live cremation of the sheep, but the children seemed transfixed by their leader, and when he uttered several unintelligible commands, the minors ceremonially hurled their torches at the firewood in Moloch's hollow stomach. Within minutes, the searing hungry fire erupted from the idol's chest like the flames of a roaring blowtorch. The reporter cupped his hands around his ears as the sheep bleated pitifully as it writhed in agony. It endured the flames until smoke poured from its mouth, then fell limp.

After the grotesque sacrifice and ceremony, Juvenal and the children – or the 'Prometheans' as he called them – went indoors, where a sumptuous banquet had been prepared. Seated next to Juvenal at the table during the feast, Robinson quizzed him about his presence at various fires in the city. By way of explanation, Juvenal said that he was a practising occultist, who experienced premonitions about the places where fires would take lives. Armed with this foreknowledge of the blazes, Juvenal was able to arrive in time to see them break out. He insisted that he had never resorted to blatant arson.

He then rambled on about the ancient Celtic feast of Samhain and the obscure rituals involving burning effigies of Judas which the Lancashire authorities were clamping down on, and of the late Dr William Price, the father of human cremation. Juvenal agreed with Price on the subject of burial, arguing that it was the antithesis of all that was aesthetic, hygienic, and scientific, and that it caused vast wastage of land and pollution.

"Sooner or later we will run out of cemetery land and we will have to either burn the dead or recycle them," Juvenal told Robinson.

Alfred Robinson doubted if his editor would ever publish these rantings of a madman, but scribbled furiously nevertheless in his shorthand note book, recording everything that was said to him.

"At midnight I will show you something very spectacular," Juvenal promised.

"What would that be, sir?"

"If your nerves can take it, I shall show you the tortured souls of Hell," replied Juvenal calmly.

At nine o'clock sharp, Juvenal and the Prometheans divested themselves of their ceremonial hats and robes. Juvenal then donned his silk top hat, a black frock coat, and a long, black, satin-lined cape. The children, on the other hand, took up their ragged clothes once more and walked barefoot out of the grand house, but at least their bellies were now full. They were all going to watch another fatal blaze that had been foreseen by their benefactor. Robinson was very sceptical about the whole affair but, sure enough, after walking for almost an hour, the seven of them came upon a blazing cottage near a place called Whiston Cross. A woman at one of the upstairs windows was screaming out for help and in desperation threw her baby, which was cocooned in several blankets, down towards the gawping children. The Prometheans made no effort to catch the baby, but Alfred Robinson leapt forward and just managed to catch the small crying bundle, clutching it to his chest.

"Jump woman!" Juvenal cackled, gazing up at the terror-stricken woman, who was coughing and choking as the smoke poured out of the open window in thick black clouds.

"Jump!" cried the Prometheans in unison.

The woman struggled to get her foot on to the window ledge in an attempt to climb out of the burning cottage, but as she did so, the flames rose up her long dress and within seconds they had engulfed her. She tried to jump, but as she did so, her dress became snagged on something and she dangled, upside down, just out of reach of any help from below, as the breeze fanned her flaming garments.

The reporter urged Juvenal and the children to help the woman, but they simply laughed and did nothing but avidly observe as the scenario unfolded. Robinson himself was forced to watch impotently as the inverted woman frantically kicked her legs as she burned alive. As soon as the flames had consumed her, the burnt dress gave way and she fell to the ground, a smouldering heap which looked barely human.

The burning cottage was in such a remote rural location, that no one came to extinguish the blaze. Juvenal and the children said nothing, their faces betraying no sympathy for either the woman or her orphaned baby. After the fire had died down to the smouldering stage, at a signal from Juvenal, they all returned to their home, the children trooping behind their evil master. The journalist followed, holding the baby and cursing Juvenal under his breath. He felt sickened and confused by the shock of witnessing the woman's horrific death.

But the worst was still to come.

Back at Juvenal's house, the traumatised journalist suggested that one of the children had been sent to start the fire at the Whiston cottage. This enraged Juvenal and he raised his cane high above his head and seemed about to bring it down on the reporter's skull, but stopped at the last moment and stood there trembling instead. He fell backwards and landed in his chair, spitting foam. He eyes fixed on the crying baby in Robinson's lap, and with a sneer suggested that it should be given up to Moloch.

"Over my dead body, Mr Juvenal," Robinson said through gritted teeth, clutching the baby even tighter to his chest.

Juvenal smiled and pretended that it had been a jest in bad taste, and offered the reporter a glass of wine.

"This baby needs medical attention," said Robinson.

The baby had not stopped crying since the fire and he thought it might have sustained an injury when it landed so heavily in his arms. He stood up and told Juvenal that he was leaving, but the eccentric old man urged him to stay until midnight, which was just half an hour away now. Robinson shook his head and said that he had seen more than enough of the goings on in the Juvenal household. He began to fear for his own life, and headed towards the door. Juvenal pleaded with him, and promised that the manifestations he would conjure up with fire and incantations would terrify but fascinate the readers of the *Chronicle*. The baby had suddenly stopped crying, and was looking placidly at him. The reporter wasn't sure what to do. Should he leave now and take the baby to a hospital, or should he wait a while longer and see what further hocus-pocus the madman was going to stage.

"Very well, Mr Robinson, we shall do it now," said Juvenal.

He stormed off and beckoned to the children to follow. They left the dining hall, and Robinson rocked the baby in front of a blazing fire as he ran through the night's strange events in his mind. Juvenal and the Prometheans returned minutes later, dressed up once again in their outlandish costumes.

"Come, sir, and see the power of eternal fire," said Juvenal.

They went outside and Juvenal lit his own torch and then lit each of the children's torches in turn. He led them to the far end of the vast garden at the rear of the house. A thick wooden beam, about six feet in length, rested on two columns of stones, and between these stones were several bales of hay, covered with brushwood. A white circle had been painted on the grass, and it encompassed the wooden beam and the hay. At various points around this circle, were written many strange words and symbols which held no meaning for Robinson, who had seen too much already and was now determined to leave Juvenal and his little mindless robots at the first opportunity.

Juvenal raised his torch to the sky and recited various phrases in an unknown language, and the children answered several times with equally strange words. Robinson was becoming increasingly restless, and was getting ready to make his escape. The torch which Juvenal held was lowered and thrust at the hay bails. The only welcoming effect was the warmth that bathed Robinson and the swathed baby. The fire quickly rose and the flames licked at the wooden beam, then one of the children suddenly swung a bucket full of inflammable liquid at the beam. It saturated the beam, and in an instant, blue white and yellow flames spat everywhere.

Robinson instinctively shielded the baby from the intense heat, and turned his back on the senseless ritual. Then he heard strange moaning voices. The children gasped in awe, and some of them started to giggle. The reporter half-turned towards the fierce fire and saw something he would never be able to explain or erase from his memory for the rest of his life. A grotesque array of scarlet and yellow faces, all grimacing in terrible agonies, were emerging from the blazing beam of wood. Some let out a stream of filthy swear words and begged for help as their faces became distorted by the flames. Some of the faces were skeletal with chattering, rattling jaws, whilst others looked human, but their skin gradually burnt away in blackened layers until only a skull was left. Some of the terrifying apparitions had arms that reached out, as if seeking help, and these would slowly melt back into flames.

Juvenal came over and explained what was transpiring to the reporter.

"That's not just any old piece of wood, it's the old hanging beam from the gallows at Kirkdale Gaol. I paid a pretty price for it. It has absorbed the souls and minds of so many evil people over the years. Look at them. Watch them suffer."

A strange gale sprang up from nowhere and blasted the fire, showering the children with sparks and glowing embers. Thunder rolled in the skies, and a hard rain started to fall. Alfred Robinson saw his chance, and dashed off, clutching the baby close to him. The sprightly Henry Juvenal immediately gave chase, and Robinson was in no doubt that he was running for his life. The fear of death and the fate of the helpless baby filled the reporter with an adrenalin rush, and he was soon able to outdistance the weird old occultist and his strange brood of tiny servants.

The reporter and the baby survived the incident, but the *London Chronicle* did not print a word of Alfred Robinson's article, because the editor considered that it was in bad taste and would be sure to result in some kind of lawsuit.

Henry Juvenal died and was unofficially cremated, according to his wishes, at Scarth Hill, near Ormskirk, in 1911. The stone idol representing Moloch in his garden was pulled down and broken up by a Presbyterian sect in 1912.

Back on Track

A calm cold night had fallen on the city of Liverpool. High above the haze of the factory smoke-stacks in the north, a full moon shone down on the night of Tuesday, 24 May 1910. Even the brilliance of the lunar orb was not sufficiently bright to blot out that mysterious ghost from the depths of time and space – Halley's Comet. The vaporous interplanetary wanderer hung stretched out in the starry arched heavens near the constellations of Gemini and Leo.

This was the twenty-ninth recorded visit of the great celestial apparition, and in her time she had looked down many times each century to witness the rise and fall of civilisations and the tardy advancement of mankind, from the days of prehistory to the building of the pyramids, from the beginnings of the Roman Empire to the French Revolution.

Upon this occasion, however, the long-tailed comet looked down on a truly pitiful sight; dozens of homeless and discarded mortals, sleeping, hunched up under thin sheets of newspaper, in the parks of the city at midnight. Perhaps a few of these unfortunate men, women and children stirred from their alfresco slumbers and caught a glimpse of the visiting comet before pulling the newspaper blankets over their faces and sinking back into the happier world of dreams.

Elsewhere in Liverpool, a policeman strolling on his measured beat was regularly eyeing the unfamiliar smudge of light in the night sky, and a few of those privileged enough to be sleeping under a roof took a thoughtful gaze at the comet through their bedroom windows before the candle was blown out.

Ethel Godwinson, a frail sixty-year-old widow, was amongst this latter group. She gazed from her bedroom window at the spectral comet in the western sky and thought about all of the panic it had engendered. She was an avid reader of the newspapers, and had read every scare-mongering article on Comet Halley. Astronomers had apparently detected poisonous cyanogen gas in the spectrum of the comet's tail and it had been predicted that the Earth would pass through it.

Fortunately, the nucleus of the comet had only approached within thirteen million miles of Earth, yet the world in its orbit had actually passed through the outer portion of Halley's tail. Luckily for the human race, the cyanogen gas had been so tenuous, that it had posed no threat to the planet.

Mrs Godwinson dwelt for a while on the unfathomable scale of outer space, the origin of the universe and the meaning of existence, before turning in for the night. She was on the brink of falling asleep when she distinctly heard a noise on the landing outside her bedroom door. As she lived alone, she knew it had to be an intruder, and she trembled in her bed. Sure enough, the door slowly creaked open, and the shadowy form of a stout man entered. Mrs Godwinson let out a stifled yelp, but in a heartbeat the fellow was upon her, holding the blade of a clasp knife to her throat.

"You make even a peep and you're dead!" he warned, in a distinctive Northern Irish accent.

Mrs Godwinson's late neighbour, old Mr McKay, had spoken in the exact same accent, being raised in Belfast, so she recognised it at once. She started to cry. The moonlight filtering in through the drawn curtains shone on the man's knife-wielding hand. That hand had half of its forefinger missing. The other hand pressed down hard on her bosom, and across the knuckles slithered the tattoo of a snake. A handkerchief covered the bottom half of the knifeman's face, and the peaked cloth cap he wore cast a shadow over the remaining half. He ordered the terrified widow to get out of bed, and he seemed to know all about the small wooden chest that was hidden under the bed and which contained the five hundred pounds of Mrs Godwinson's life savings. Kicking her viciously in the ribs, he ordered her to drag the chest out. Cringing from the blows, she pulled it out and he ordered her to open it.

The overweight thug was soon stuffing the money into his pockets, and Mrs Godwinson felt some relief – at least her ordeal would soon be over now that he had got what he wanted. Not a bit of it! The burglar started slapping her hard across the face, and warned her that if she tried to raise the alarm after he had left, he'd come back and slit her throat. He then left the bedroom.

The police were not contacted until the following morning, when the bruised and battered widow finally dared to venture out of her bedroom. Not only had the nine-and-a-half fingered thief taken all her savings, he had also stolen her jewellery, which had been kept in a velvet-lined box in a cabinet in the parlour. Amongst the jewellery was a distinctive gold St Christopher's medal which had been in her family for generations.

Ethel's thirty-five-year-old son Michael swore he would somehow track down the cowardly burglar who had reduced his frail widowed mother into a nervous wreck. Ethel suffered terrible nightmares about the burglar, and would wake up screaming in the night.

The police knew of no one in the underworld who matched the man's description, and as the weeks went by, no progress was made by the detectives on the case.

In July of that year, just two months after the robbery, a curious coincidence took place. A priest visited the Everton home of Ethel Godwinson, and during the long conversation he had with the widow, he told of an old superstition associated with St Christopher – the saint featured on the medal which the burglar had stolen. Years ago, in Ireland, when people wanted to find money that had been lost or stolen, they'd say: "Saint Christopher, Saint Christopher, return that which is rightly mine!" After uttering this, a reversal of the misfortune would take place, and the missing or stolen items would soon be recovered. This was because Saint Christopher was the patron saint of lost causes and mislaid objects.

Mrs Godwinson duly recited the saint's name twice over and asked for her savings and jewellery to be returned. She had no faith that the incantation would work, but she recited it more for the sake of the priest than anything else. This all took place at half-past one in the afternoon.

At that precise time, a short but broad and muscular man in a cloth cap entered the dark warren of shops and offices at Tuton Chambers, 44 Lime Street, and walked upstairs to a tattooing studio. The man was Rory Kavanagh, and he told the tattoo artist precisely what he wanted in a raw Northern Irish accent. Kavanagh wanted a picture of a naked woman lying stretched out across his back. The Irishman pointed to the framed drawing of the woman in question hanging on the wall. When he pointed at her, he pointed with half a forefinger. The tattoo artist – Michael Godwinson – also noticed the writhing green serpent tattooed across the knuckles of the man's other hand.

When Kavanagh stripped to the waist, Michael instantly noticed the distinctive oversized Saint Christopher medal hanging on a chain from his neck. He recognised it immediately as the one stolen from his mother, and the man wearing it was the very brute who had held the knife to her throat that night in May. Michael Godwinson managed to keep calm on the outside, but beneath the composed exterior, he was seething and had to suppress a strong desire to batter the Irishman's head in. Instead of which, he exacted a very unusual revenge upon the robber.

Instead of tattooing a naked lady upon Kavanagh's fleshy back, Michael Godwinson used his needles to inscribe, in capital letters, the sentence, 'I AM A THIEF AND A WOMAN BEATER' in a very aesthetic-looking font, straight across the Irishman's back. After Michael had finished the last letter, he made an excuse to leave the room and he called for a policeman. Kavanagh was subsequently arrested, and although he had already spent a quarter of Mrs Godwinson's life-savings, the rest of the money and most of the jewellery was recovered, along with the loot from some of Kavanagh's other cowardly crimes.

Rory Kavanagh was given twelve years' hard labour for his crimes, and for the rest of his life, he carried the tattooed words of shame on his back.

Dead Ringer

I have collected many tales from priests and ministers from all denominations, both serving and retired, who have tackled terrifying beings of a supernatural nature. An elderly priest related the following account to me a few years back.

One pleasant evening in the autumn of 1977, a middle-aged woman called at a Catholic priest's house in a certain suburb of Liverpool, and was soon invited in. The woman's name was Linda, and she was a regular churchgoer and a devout Catholic. Father Mark sat her down at the table of his living quarters and poured her a strong cup of tea. He could see that Linda was trembling, and looked as if she hadn't slept in days. Father Mark was in his early twenties and had only recently been ordained. Nothing in all the years of his theology studies could have prepared him for what Linda revealed to him that evening.

"My husband has returned from the grave, and he's making my life hell," she said, the teacup she held with her shaking hand rattling against the saucer.

Father Mark was dumbfounded, and quite lost for words. He realised that it was not a priest that Linda required, but a psychiatrist. Yet he was still stuck for words, because the woman facing him was a lovable person who had done a great deal for local charities and was usually to be found behind the counter of the local Oxfam shop.

Luckily, a senior priest – Father Maxwell – came into the house at that moment, and after he had said hello to Linda, Father Mark took him aside and led him into the kitchen. He whispered the words the woman had uttered to him a minute before, and Father Max (as they called him) reacted with his usual pensive expression. He scratched his silvery hair and squinted in contemplation through his wire-framed spectacles.

"I'll see to this, Father Mark. You make a fresh pot of tea."

Father Max re-entered the living room and sat facing Linda. They exchanged a few pleasantries, then with great sincerity, Father Max encouraged Linda to talk about her problem. Linda said that two weeks ago, a man had called at her home late at night claiming to be her dead husband. He looked identical to her husband in every way and spoke exactly like him, but Linda's husband had died five years ago, just before she came to the parish. Linda had almost passed out when she had seen him on her doorstep.

"And how did this man explain away the fact that your husband was at rest?" inquired Father Max, sensitively.

"He said it had all been a terrible misunderstanding," Linda stammered, tightly gripping the cup.

Her eyes darted to the left and right as she seemed to search for the appropriate words to describe the strange incident.

"A misunderstanding?" frowned Father Max, gazing over to the doorway and seeing Father Mark pouring water into the teapot.

Linda then continued to relate the rest of her bizarre account.

"Yes, I know it sounds crazy, Father, but that's what he's making out. He said he had a twin brother and that I had been living with his twin. They'd swapped places when he had decided to leave me. His twin agreed to come over from Australia and take his place. I don't really believe any of it, but this man who has now moved in with me, is the spitting image of my late husband."

"Do you sleep together?" Father Max asked bluntly, and noticed Father Mark looking in at him from the kitchen with his mouth wide open in astonishment.

"No, Father ... we have separate beds, ... but he won't leave me alone ... he's always bothering me," said Linda blushing somewhat.

"This is a most extraordinary situation, Linda. Did your husband have an identical twin to your knowledge?" Father Max asked.

"He couldn't have," Linda replied. "He would have mentioned it to me, surely? No twin ever came to our wedding."

Father Max placed his palms together and touched his chin with the joined middle fingers as he meditated on the matter.

"I take it you have tested the truth of what he is saying by asking him to recall incidents in your life known only to you and your late husband?"

"Yes,. That's just it. He seems to know everything, Father; every little personal memory and private joke," Linda said.

"The only way we could prove or disprove what he says is by comparing his dental records with those of your late husband's," Father Max suggested.

"Oh, no! They wouldn't have to exhume him or anything, would they?" Linda sniffled.

"Oh, no, no, Linda. Nothing of the sort."

Father Max reached over and gave her taut fist a reassuring squeeze and Father Mark eventually came in with a fresh pot of tea. While the tea was being poured, Linda said to both priests, "I feel as if I'm going mad!"

"Oh don't worry, Linda," said Father Mark. "Father Max will sort things out."

That very night, at 10pm, the two priests accompanied Linda back to her home to confront the living carbon copy of her dead husband, Alan. As the priests approached the house, they saw the shadow of Linda's alleged husband glide across the parlour curtains. Moments later, the front door opened as Linda was taking her door keys from her handbag.

"Good evening, Fathers," said the man calling himself Alan. He wore a relaxed and bemused look, giving the impression that he had been expecting the late night visit.

"Evening," said Father Max curtly, as he followed Linda into the house, who in turn was followed by Father Mark.

The two priests stood in the hallway, staring constantly at Alan, a small bald-headed man of about fifty-five years of age. The four of them went into the parlour, and the priests sat facing Alan across the dining table. Linda left to hang up her coat, then quickly returned to the parlour, eager to see what Father Max was going to do to resolve her remarkable dilemma.

Father Max asked Alan to give his date of birth, and a correct reply was given.

"Can you recall your national insurance number?' Father Max queried, and fixed Alan with an intense gaze.

"What is this?" sighed Alan, "The Spanish Inquisition?"

"Just answer please," insisted Father Max.

"L ... R ..." Alan struggled at first, but then reeled off the rest of the alphanumeric code with no apparent difficulty.

It was found to be correct.

The questions and answers went on for almost an hour. Why had Alan decided to leave Linda and swap places with his brother? It had become a stifling, stale marriage, according to Alan. Hadn't the twin brother from Australia a suspicious accent? No, he had only lived down under for four years and had never developed an accent. What did the wife of Alan's twin brother say when she discovered that her husband had died? His twin brother wasn't married, was Alan's reply.

Alan had a ready answer for every question Father Max threw at him, and he seemed so smug. Father Max thought a great deal about the situation and at one point even wondered whether Alan might be telling the truth. Yet there was something very eerie in the man's eyes – something which kept his suspicions alive.

Linda looked across at the elder priest and he rose from the chair and beckoned her into the hallway. He pulled the parlour door to and suggested looking into the matter again in the morning.

"Oh please, Father Max. Don't go now," Linda implored.

"I was thinking about going to the police in the morning to check out the records of his twin in Australia. At least we could then establish whether or not he did actually exist," Father Max told Linda, then saw the disappointment and desperation in her eyes.

"Do you believe what he says, or do you think he's some sort of conman?" she asked.

"I'm not sure. There's something about him that I can't quite put my finger on," said the priest.

"What do you mean, Father?"

The priest shrugged then looked at his wristwatch and went back into the parlour to find Alan deep in conversation with Father Mark. Alan was asking the young priest if he ever felt like sleeping with a woman.

"No, to be honest," said Father Mark, "I don't really think about it."

Alan persisted with his impertinent line of questioning. "Are you gay then?" he asked.

"No, I am not, and that's getting a bit personal isn't it?" said Father Mark, who was getting very twitchy and agitated, and obviously did not quite know how to deal with him.

Father Max could sense the mischief in Alan, or whoever – or whatever – he was. He had met his kind before, but he didn't want to alarm Linda or Father Mark just yet.

"Do you think of women, Father?" Alan asked with a sly grin, turning towards Father Max.

The older of the two priests, who with his age and experience was more than a match for him, sat down and said, "Yes, of course I do. I think of Joan of Arc and Mary Magdalene ..."

"Promiscuous women," Alan said, and laughed.

"Tell me, Alan. Do you believe in God?" Father Max asked him.

"No it's all lies. Escapism, that's what it is. You die, decompose, then you go down a cold muddy hole and you're forgotten about."

"What do you believe in?" Father Mark asked.

"To be honest – Hitler," Alan said, revelling at the shocked expression on Linda's face.

"Hitler was evil, and like a man possessed," said Father Max.

The priest gave a telltale smirk that Father Mark recognised all too well by now. It meant that Father Max had something up his sleeve.

"That's nonsense," said Alan, who seemed to have an answer for everything. "Freud proved that so-called possession was just a personality disorder. You priests used to burn people with psychiatric illnesses."

Alan stood up in front of the gas fire as he spouted the words.

"I can't redress the wrongs of the extremists ..." Father Max said.

"Then what's the difference between the Third Reich extremists and Hitler and your Pope and the Jesuits? Answer that!" Alan snarled, grinning broadly.

"Very well, let's say you're completely right. Can you disprove the existence of

God? Never mind the failings and shortcomings of mankind – what about God?" said Father Max.

"There is no God! There never has been!" Alan ranted.

"There is a God!" Linda shouted back.

"Linda, where was God when your mother died in agony from cancer? She begged to be killed with an overdose of morphine! She prayed and no help came."

Alan seemed so enraged by the injustice of it all, that he was now foaming at the mouth.

"How would you know? She died alone," Linda told him.

A hard, revealing silence descended on the room.

Alan didn't answer. He stared at Father Max.

"Why did you choose Linda?" the old priest asked, giving Alan a penetrating look.

"What do you mean? I chose her because I loved her. I first set eyes on her when she was working at Littlewoods Pools …"

"No, I mean why did you, as a demon, choose to come and ruin this innocent woman's life? You're no more her late husband than I am."

Father Max seethed as he spoke these words, and he rose from the chair and took a small silver crucifix from his inside jacket pocket. He pointed the cross at the argumentative enigma.

Father Mark slowly got to his feet and trembled.

"What are you talking about, you silly old man?" sneered Alan, but he backed away, his eyes fixed on the thrust-out crucifix as if it were a loaded pistol.

"In the name of Jesus Christ, I abjure thee and summon thee to leave here at once. In the name of Jesus Christ, the Son of God …"

Alan's face twisted unnaturally and changed. He let loose a string of obscenities and profanities, and spat at Father Max. He accused the priest of being a child molester and a rapist, and claimed that he had committed various repulsive sexual acts. Father Max was unabashed by the words, and bravely continued to walk slowly towards Alan, still carrying the crucifix in his outstretched arms. Alan then turned on Father Mark and accused him of stealing money from his own mother.

"That's a lie!" Father Mark shouted back.

"You'll be dead before you're thirty, believe me!" Alan screamed, "And then you'll be dragged down into the bowels of the earth to meet the real god!"

Linda staggered from the parlour into the hall in a daze, she walked to the telephone on the half-moon table, all the time feeling as if she was moving in slow motion. Mechanically, she dialled 999. As she was telling the operator that she needed the police urgently, there was a heart-stopping scream in the parlour that echoed throughout the house. Linda dropped the receiver and ran back into the parlour. Alan was nowhere to be seen and Father Max was holding Father Mark in his arms on the floor. Linda screamed and asked what had happened to him. Father Max said he had merely fainted from the shock of seeing the demon reveal itself. It had finally discarded the disguise of Rita's deceased husband and had appeared in its real terrifying form, before vanishing back to where it had come from – the infernal regions of Hell.

"Linda! Linda!" came a deep resonant voice from somewhere up in the chimney. It filled the poor woman with dread – was the monster coming back? Father Mark soon regained consciousness and looked around in horror, expecting the agent of Satan to still be around. Father Max and Linda helped him to his feet, and they all left the house together.

Linda stayed at the priests' house until she could find alternative accommodation. She asked Father Max repeatedly why a demon had chose to imitate her late husband, and why had he picked on her? Father Max said he honestly did not know, but in his own experience, such evil beings picked on the devout followers of Christ as much as the disbelieving atheists. Presumably, there was some sinister method in their madness.

When Linda dared to venture back into her house with Fathers Max and Mark and the removal men, she immediately noticed that all of her religious statues of the Sacred Heart and the Blessed Virgin Mary had been turned round so that they faced the wall.

Father Max later heard about another tragic case of a woman in Page Moss who ended up in a psychiatric hospital because she believed that her sister was an impostor. The woman was apparently diagnosed as a being schizophrenic and was suffering from the mental disorder known as Capgras's Syndrome, although she had not suffered any mental health problems before in her life. She was apparently convinced that her younger sister had been replaced by an identical-looking impostor.

Whether or not the sister was a sinister replacement of the same kind as the one in the previous account will probably never be known.

Mysteries of the Deep

A visitor from another world may find it strange that we call our planet Earth, when in fact over two-thirds of our planet's surface area is submerged under water. The vast oceans that cover the Earth are mostly unexplored, and there are undoubtedly many unknown sea creatures in their depths that marine biologists have yet to discover.

In 1938, a large fish called the Coelacanth was caught in the Indian Ocean. The huge, fearsome-looking fish, which was swimming the seas when the dinosaurs ruled the Earth, was thought to have become extinct seventy millions of years ago. If the Coelacanth survived the age of the dinosaurs, could larger creatures have also survived and perhaps still be roaming the ocean bed?

As late as 1991, Smithsonian and Peruvian scientists described a new species of beaked whale that had previously gone undetected in the oceans of the world. New discoveries of various species of sea creature are regularly made, and some think that the Loch Ness Monster and the sea serpents of old maritime folklore may have a basis in fact. In this part of the world, there have been numerous well-documented encounters with unidentified sea creatures, and many of the incidents took place in Merseyside and Wirral waters.

In the 1880s, on several occasions, fishermen spotted a long, snake-like creature, with eleven humps, cruising from the River Dee towards Liverpool Bay. A Justice of the Peace from Liverpool, vacationing in Llandudno in 1882, sighted the same humped 'sea monster' and later signed an affidavit stating that it was over three hundred feet in length, and was swimming out towards Liverpool Bay. Eight other people walking along the promenade at Llandudno saw the same large creature.

For centuries, fishermen in Cardigan Bay have claimed that a sea serpent, which they call Morgwar, patrols the Irish Sea. Curiously, the Cornish fishermen also call their legendary sea monster Morgwar. Legend has it that Morgwar belonged to a race of monsters from the north, and that one of these serpents, also referred to as a dragon, had a lair in a riverside cave. According to some mediaeval maps, this cave was located near to modern day Ellesmere Port, and in the days of King Arthur, Sir Gawain, an outstanding Knight of the Round Table, set off to slay the monster, which was causing havoc with the local fishing community. Sir Gawain chased the monster into what is now Delamere Forest and killed it.

In modern times there have been a few alleged encounters with a spine-chilling creature at West Kirby, which were explained away as figments of the imagination and urban legend, but I'm not so sure.

The first report comes from a thirteen-year-old Susan Rogers from Liverpool, who was visiting Hilbre Island in the winter of 1954 with her eighteen-year-old cousin, Tina Jones. Apparently, Susan had a row with Tina on the island and ran off to hide. Tina searched everywhere for her cousin and shouted out to her, warning her that the tide would soon be coming in, leaving the island cut off from the mainland.

Meanwhile, Susan went sulking into the 'Ladies' Cave' on the island as the rain-laden skies turned ever gloomier. Susan was gazing out from the cave to see if Tina was looking for her – when she heard an unusual rattling sound. At first she thought the sound was just the pattering of rain on the rocks, as the skies opened and there was a sudden downpour. Then something touched the girl's bare ankle. She looked down and saw what looked like a dark brown length of cane covered with stiff bristles, quivering between her sandals. She spun round in fright and was met by something truly horrifying; a huge crustacean, about four feet high and six feet wide, was standing on four, perhaps even six, jointed legs. It was grey and clad in an armour of segmented shells, but the most frightening thing about it was the pair of massive blood-red eyes which swivelled around in its head. Susan almost passed out with fear.

The strange, bristled cane-like thing, which was now prodding at her skirt, turned out to be one of two antennae which were attached to the head of the monstrosity. Its mouth clacked opened and closed with a rattling sound and its legs clicked and clattered as it lunged forward. Susan leapt from the cave mouth and landed awkwardly on the rain-slicked rocks below, spraining her ankle. She still couldn't scream – her vocal cords were paralysed – and she almost blacked out twice as she scrambled madly across the beach, because she could still hear the ominous clattering rattle of the beast in the distance.

Tina found her in a sorry state, cowering behind a boulder, crouched on all fours and as pale as death. She shuddered when Susan told her about the 'thing' in the cave. The mysterious shelled creature was allegedly seen on several more occasions at Hilbre Island in the 1960s, and there is even one report of a similar creature being washed ashore on Parkgate promenade during a fierce storm in the late 1940s. Men delivering beer to a waterfront pub said the crab-like creature was some seven feet in length, and it kicked furiously on its back until a wave crashed over the promenade and righted it. The weird-looking creature then crawled sideways back into the sea.

A *Liverpool Echo* newspaper clipping I received from a reader about a waterfront junk yard in northern Liverpool in the 1970s stated that two junkmen were clearing out part of the yard when they spotted some brown-skinned creature flitting beneath a mound of rusting scrap. This organism looked something like an octopus with very long thin tentacles. Some of the scrap metal parts at the bottom of the heap dated back to the 1940s, and had lain undisturbed for years, and it appeared that something had made its home beneath all the junk. The two junkmen could hear something moving about and breathing "like a pair of bellows" beneath the scrap pile, and they even called for assistance to remove the scrap from two mechanics from a nearby garage.

Night soon fell, and the scrap was finally removed by the light from a fire in a brazier and a homemade torch made from paraffin-soaked cloth tied to a length of pipe. There was a hole, nine inches across, in the yard floor where the scrap had been piled, and peering from this hole was an eye of some sort. The four men jumped back in horror when a thin, wormlike tentacle slithered out and tried to drag a piece of an old car alternator over the hole. The burning torch was thrust at the tentacle, and one of the junkyard men brought an air rifle from a hut and fired a .22 slug down the hole. The creature let out a faint squeal and moments later, another squeaking sound was heard coming from a sewer grid in the street just outside the junkyard.

I mentioned this case on the radio and two people telephoned to say that they worked in a junkyard in 1975 and remembered hearing about the weird creature under the scrap-yard. When the yard was later excavated to make way for the building of a new premises, a slick of grease and oil that had filtered down from the scrap over the years had formed, and in this layer of greasy mulch, the remains of what looked like a huge decomposed jellyfish was found. Unfortunately, no marine biologist was called for to examine the remains. The Philistine workers simply tossed the mysterious creature into a skip.

Double Trouble

Some occultists say that we all have a ghostly twin, or doppelganger, but the twin usually keeps out of sight in normal circumstances. However, when we are ill, over-stressed, or experiencing a great crisis of some kind, our doppelganger is increasingly likely to manifest itself, and tradition states that if you see your own double, you will be dead within a year. I have been researching the phenomenon of doppelgangers long enough to know that the appearance of a flesh and blood replica of a person hardly ever spells doom, and the following little gem is a case in point.

It was the marriage twenty-two-year-old Catherine Emily Cox had dreamt about for over five years, and on the sunny Saturday morning of 14 January 1882, the dream became a reality. She stood with James Walker before the altar of St Werburgh's on Grange Road, Birkenhead, and the minister had only just started to recite the words of the wedding ceremony. He solemnly intoned the usual declaration, "If any man can show any just cause why these two people may not be joined together, let him speak now, or forever hold his peace."

A man shouted, "Stop!" from the back of the church. The voice belonged to a tall stout police constable who came hurrying down the aisle with his truncheon drawn. Women gasped in astonishment, and some wondered if the policeman was some secret jealous lover of Catherine Emily. However, PC Williams was after James Walker. He grabbed at the lapels of the astonished bridegroom's expensive suit and said, "Got you! Now down to the station with you!"

"What the devil are you talking about?" protested James Walker, furiously.

"Gawd! The gall of you! It's always the same with you jokers when you get caught isn't it? Not laughing now are you?" said the deep-voiced policeman, staring Walker straight in the eyes, with an expression just as angry as the bridegroom's.

The best man, John Porter, stepped forward and asked the policeman what Mr Walker was being arrested for, and the constable said that Walker had knocked his hat off in Birkenhead Park less than quarter of an hour ago, and he had chased him to the church; all the way to St Werburgh's. Apparently, the mischievous James Walker had even turned to pull faces at his pursuer, and had taunted him with obscene language.

The poor bride, Catherine Emily, looked unsteady on her feet, as if she was about to faint.

"But, officer, you are mistaken," argued John Porter, "because my friend has been in this church for the past half hour, and most of the people here will confirm this."

The minister, the best man, several guests and members of the Walker family, stated that James Walker had indeed been at the church for the last half hour, waiting for his bride, who had been long overdue. Before that, Walker had been at home preparing for the ceremony, and there were several respectable witnesses who could vouch for his whereabouts.

"Then you've got a twin brother with the same red carnation in his lapel, sir," said PC Williams, flushing with embarrassment.

Reluctantly he let go of the bridegroom, then turned and walked out of the church with as much dignity as he could muster under the circumstances.

John Porter looked at his friend Walker and said, "If that policeman only knew how right he was!"

Porter was well aware of James Walker's troublesome doppelganger – a sinister ghostly twin that had haunted the bridegroom since his teens. On one of the most important days of his life, Walker's double had almost ruined the wedding. The cheeky doppelganger allegedly even made love to James Walker's wife a year later! Catherine Emily Walker did not realise what had occurred until she heard footsteps coming up the stairs of her home one night. She trembled and hid under the blankets, thinking it was a burglar. Instead, her husband came into the room, apologising for the delay in getting home from his office. Catherine was baffled, as she had retired early to bed with her 'husband', and the couple had just made love. Catherine suddenly noticed that there was no one lying next to her in the bed, and it gradually dawned on her that her husband's accursed double had masqueraded as James.

Walker had many theories about his badly-behaved carbon copy counterpart, including one conjecture that the doppelganger was actually the ghost of his twin brother who died at the age of two. There is also a report that the doppelganger out-lived the original copy, as it was allegedly spotted amongst the mourners at the graveside during James Walker's funeral in the 1930s.

A Change of Fortune

One rainy evening, in September 1862, two women walked down Brownlow Hill towards the grim towering buildings of the Liverpool Workhouse. The women were Margaret Jones, aged seventy, and her thirty-five-year-old daughter, Mary Taylor, the mother of six children. Grey haired, bent and feeble, the widow Maggie Jones hugged her daughter at the workhouse door and surveyed the young woman's careworn face.

"Here, Mary," said Mrs Jones, removing her wedding ring from her bony finger. "Take this."

"No, Mam, I'll not have that!" protested Mary, seizing the ring and placing it back on the finger where it had been proudly worn for over fifty years.

"You could pawn it, my lovely," said Mrs Jones, tears welling in her grey-blue eyes.

"I'll get by somehow, Mam, but certainly not by selling your wedding ring," said Mary, and she too started to cry. "Oh mother, I don't want you to go into that place, you know I don't," Mary looked with despair at the workhouse door. "Please come back home with me."

"I'd only be a burden on you and Jim. You and he have mouths to feed and Jim's out of work. My health is bad as well. It's not so bad in here, love, they give me medicine," Margaret Jones told her sniffling daughter.

The old lady rang the bell, and a pauper janitor opened the small gate in the main heavy oaken door. Mother and daughter embraced, and then went their separate ways. At least Mary had enjoyed her mother's day out from the abominable workhouse, but the future looked so bleak. Husband Jim was out of work, and her children were walking around barefoot.

When Mary Taylor reached her little home off London Road, she saw Jim and his friend Mick talking in hushed tones by the fireside. As she stoked up the fire, she overheard something that made her heart leap. Jim and Mick were discussing a robbery. As Mary cooked potatoes for the children, Jim came into the kitchen, and told her about the plan. He and Mick intended to rob the house of a rich merchant in south Liverpool the following evening. Mary begged him not to do it, but Jim told her he had to, or they'd all starve. Each day Jim had trudged down to the docks and begged for work, but to no avail, and finding a job elsewhere was well nigh impossible. So it was robbery or the workhouse for Jim Taylor.

That night, in bed, Mary cried bitter tears, and at one point got up and pleaded with God to change her luck. She didn't want her husband to go to prison.

"Please, Lord, I need money so desperately," she whispered. "I don't know where to turn."

That same night, an old man called at the Liverpool Workhouse with several sacks of potatoes and bags of flour. He said they'd been sent from Hillside Farm in Childwall for the harvest festival at the workhouse. From nine o'clock in the evening until one in the morning, Margaret Jones was told to peel the potatoes in three of the sacks with another old woman. This task was completed, and on the following morning, Mrs Jones asked to see her daughter, and a priest who knew the family visited Mary Taylor and told her to go to the workhouse. Mrs Jones hugged her daughter when she saw her, then told her about a strange occurrence.

At midnight, her hands red and sore from hours of peeling, she had picked up yet another of the potatoes to peel, and found it to be as heavy as a stone. She inserted the knife, which hit something hard in the centre of the potato. Curious to find out what it was, she cut the potato in half and prised out a large nugget of what seemed to be gold. She washed it under the tap and it shone brilliantly, so she slipped it into her apron pocket and carried on with her work, hardly able to contain her excitement. What if it really was gold? She would be able to leave the workhouse and take care of Mary and her family.

Mary took the four-inch long nugget to a trustworthy jeweller – it was the real thing, and weighed nine Troy ounces. It was exceptionally pure and worth over a thousand pounds. Margaret gave the nugget to her poverty-stricken daughter and it changed all their lives. Jim Taylor didn't have to burgle the house in Aigburth and their future was secured.

When the Childwall farmer was told about the gold that had been found in one of his potatoes, he looked puzzled and insisted that he had sent no food for any harvest festival. The old man who had delivered the potatoes to the workhouse was never seen again, and Mrs Jones and her daughter Mary were convinced that he had been an angel of mercy.

The Moon Man at the Pier Head

The following story is derived from the many letters and emails I have received from readers over the years about their reminiscences about a mysterious man who was something of a prophet and a cosmologist.

Sunday mornings at the Pier Head in the 1960s could be quite entertaining, when various speakers took to their soap boxes. Anarchists, philosophers, religious maniacs, zealous promoters of Esperanto – in fact anyone with a message – were often seen at Liverpool's equivalent of Hyde Park's Speakers' Corner.

On one particular sunny Sunday morning in 1964, a portly man in his fifties stepped on to a milk crate, and a dozen or so people gathered around to hear what he had to say. The speaker wore an astrakhan collared overcoat and a black homburg hat, the attire of the well-known television comedian, Tony Hancock. He spoke in a fine, perfectly enunciated Etonian accent, but what he talked about was strange and seemingly far-fetched. He claimed that he belonged to a race that lived inside the Moon. "You may call me a Lunarian, or a Selenite, if you wish," said the speaker.

Everyone in the crowd either laughed or sneered upon hearing this. The first manned lunar landing was still five years away, and most people were ignorant of the workings of the Solar System and the human race's place in the cosmos. Among the assembled listeners, there was a revivalist preacher, impatiently waiting to take to his own turn on the soap box, and he became incensed at the 'Moon Man's' preposterous claims. According to the speaker, the Moon was a gigantic, ancient spaceship which had brought mankind to this planet in the remote past.

"The Earth was without form and void at that time, you may recall, if you know your Genesis," said the 'Lunarian'.

The preacher gasped and clutched his Bible as if it had been physically attacked.

"You see, this planet was deeply cratered and had all sorts of monsters roaming about its surface, but he whom you would choose to call God, disposed of all the dinosaurs and landscaped the planet," said the well-spoken speaker.

"Blasphemy and lies! Don't listen to him!" cried the scandalised revivalist.

"Hush!" said an old man. "Hear him out."

The speaker continued, even though the self-proclaimed minister constantly interrupted him with shouts of "Agent of Satan!" and "False prophet!"

The crowd grew in size as the obviously well-educated and apparently eccentric man waxed lyrical about the celestial origins of mankind. The Moon would be found to have a thick metal shell beneath its lunar rock, he said. The Moon's craters were formed from the many collisions it had endured with asteroids during its long journeys through space, although some of the craters were the result of explosions caused by atomic weaponry during the 'War in Heaven' mentioned in the Bible, when the angels of Lucifer and Michael fought one another for control of the Earth.

One side of the Moon always faces the Earth, because the lunar satellite's period of rotation, and its orbit around our planet, take the same amount of time – yet some of the craters of the Moon are facing the Earth. This meant that long ago, rebels from the Earth fired atomic missiles at the Moon. All of this happened so long ago, that mankind today had no knowledge of the great events of the past.

From deep within the Moon's interior, the space people had sent various people to Earth over the centuries, on missions to re-establish contact with their descendants. Perhaps Jesus of Nazareth had been one of these messengers, the speaker conjectured. The Bible thumping minister was outraged at the suggestion and heckled the Lunarian even more loudly.

"Did Jesus not say that his kingdom was not of this world?" the speaker asked him.

The minister started to heckle even more enthusiastically, and told the crowd to turn to God. Space flight was flying in the face of the Lord, according to the minister, and all attempts at visiting the Moon would end in death and disaster, because man's place was on this planet in God's scheme of things.

The Moon Man disagreed, and made a prophetic statement.

"In the next decade, sir, a piece of the Moon will be brought down from space to this city."

Many years later, in the 1970s, NASA lent a piece of moon rock to Liverpool Museum, and the sample was put on show at the planetarium in William Brown Street. The rock, brought 240,000 miles from the Moon to our world by astronauts, is still on show at the Space and Time Gallery on the third floor of Liverpool Museum. I often make a pilgrimage to see that rock, and pieces of Mars that have fallen to Earth as meteorites, and I often wonder about the Moon Man at the Pier Head. Who was he? A knowledgeable crank? Or was he really from the Moon? What became of him? No one seems to know.

*

The astronauts of the historic Apollo Programme left behind various seismic sensors on the Moon, and when the spent parts of the moonships were deliberately sent crashing into the lunar surface, the Moon rang like a bell – as if it was hollow. Just one example of this occurred in April 1970, during the near fatal Apollo 13 mission, when a spent, 15-tonne third stage of the Saturn V launch vehicle was deliberately sent crashing down on to the Moon. A clanging sound was clearly detected by the lunar seismometers, indicating that the moon had a metallic shell beneath its cratered surface. Furthermore, strange glowing lights and shadows have been observed by astronomers for centuries on the Moon, and have never been satisfactorily explained. Sir Patrick Moore has even seen these lights, which he calls transient lunar phenomena.

Journey into Fear

In July 2002, two Liverpool men, twenty-five-year-old Jimmy Kinley and his thirty-nine-year-old cousin, Tony Reid, were enjoying a day out at Blackpool, when they got into trouble with a gang of six thugs from Southport. The argument had started when the Southport heavies overheard Jimmy Kinley's Liverpudlian accent in a pub. They started to sing offensive songs about Everton and Liverpool football clubs, and, as Jimmy was a red-hot LFC supporter, and his cousin was a dyed-in-the-wool bluenose, a slanging match ensued. Several Liverpudlian youths in the bar came to Jimmy and Tony's aid, and the situation became so tense, that the pub licensee threatened to call the police. The Southport gang left, followed by Jimmy and Tony.

In the pub car park, Jimmy started jeering at the six yobs who had returned to their two vehicles – a black transit van and a silver Honda Civic. The publican came over to Jimmy and Tony and warned them to leave as quickly as possible, as the gang they'd just had an altercation with were notorious for their violence. Jimmy got into his old white Ford Fiesta, but Tony stood outside the vehicle by the open passenger door, staring at the angry faces of the gang in their vehicles. The Transit crawled off down the road, followed just as slowly by the Honda and both vehicles stopped at the very end of the road.

"Hey, mate!" came a voice from behind the Fiesta. Tony turned to see a man in his twenties with a shaven head. He wore a black tracksuit. "You'll never make it back to Liverpool. We'll run you off the road and then kill you!" said the young man, menacingly. He then walked out of the car park. Tony shouted several profanities at the man, and then quickly climbed into the Fiesta. He turned to his worried-looking cousin. "Did you hear that?"

Jimmy nodded, then started to bite his nails.

"Think we should call the police?" Tony suggested, and felt for his mobile phone in his trouser pocket.

"No, it'd make it worse and they'd think we were scared."

Jimmy started the car and removed the handbrake as he kept an eye on the gang in their vehicles in the distance.

"We'll have to go home by an different route, Jimmy," said Tony, fastening his seat belt.

"What d'you mean?" queried Jimmy.

"We can't go down the M55, or down the A80-thingy road, because they'll be expecting us to go that way. We'll go through the B roads," Tony said.

"That'll take ages. They won't try anything, it's all macho talk."

But the Transit and the Honda stuck to them like leeches and followed them as far as Preston. Then Tony heard a bleeping sound in his trouser pocket. It was his mobile phone's battery alarm, notifying him that the phone was almost drained of power.

The Fiesta tore down the A59 towards Tarleton, and the thugs followed in hot pursuit. Then came the downpour, and Tony urged his cousin to turn left at a fork in the road.

"Why?" Jimmy asked, nervously glancing at their pursuers in the rear view mirror.

"Just do it now, will you?" said Tony, with much urgency in his voice.

So the Fiesta crossed over to the A59, and the black van and the silver car turned right, and headed down the A565 to Southport. At last they had shaken them off.

By now it was getting dark, the rain had turned to a drizzle, and Jimmy found himself on unfamiliar roads near the district of Rufford.

"I think this road leads to Ormskirk," said Tony, squinting at the hedges and trees flitting past, searching for a road sign.

"You *think*!"

Jimmy was annoyed that they had backed down to the troublemakers. God only knew how long it would take to get back to Liverpool now.

"They might have had guns. Did you think of that, Jimmy?' said Tony in an effort to try and justify telling Jimmy to take the long-winded route.

It seemed to be a road without end. A dark country lane bounded by tall hedges and the silhouettes of overhanging tree branches. Through gaps in the hedges all they could make out were fields, but there were no signposts to tell them where they were.

All of a sudden, a huge owl-like bird flew out of the darkness and hurtled towards the Fiesta's windscreen. Jimmy and Tony braced themselves for the impact, but at the last minute the strange winged creature vanished.

"What the ... ?" Jimmy gasped, dumbfounded.

"What the heck was that?"

Through the windscreen wipers, Tony could make out some dark object further down the lane. It was the shadowy figure of a long-haired woman in a flowing calf-length dress. She was standing right in the middle of the road, and the Fiesta was travelling too fast to stop in time. Jimmy instinctively slammed on the brakes anyway, and in the seconds before the impact was due, he wondered why the woman wouldn't get out of the way. As the bonnet made contact with her, she disappeared into thin air.

The car careered down the lane and eventually came to a halt at the side of a ditch. Jimmy twisted round in his seat and looked behind, while Tony wound down the passenger window and peered out into the darkness. Neither of them could see any trace of the woman they'd just run into, but they both distinctly heard an unearthly howl of laughter from somewhere down the lane, followed by a chattering of voices and cackles.

The two lads looked at each other in total disbelief, could their night out get any worse? Unfortunately, yes, because as Jimmy put the car into gear and moved off at speed down the lane, strange bat-like objects with large black flapping wings flew at the car and thudded against the windows and bodywork. Jimmy saw a pale grinning face in the offside and rear-view mirrors, and Tony felt an icy coldness "pass through" him. In addition, both men experienced what they later described as a feeling of intense dread, as if they were about to lose their lives.

Eventually, the lane curved round and joined on to a bigger road where other traffic was travelling, and the two lads were mightily relieved to leave the spooky lane full of apparitions and shadows behind them. Days later, they went in search of the lane during the safer hours of daylight, but were unable to locate it.

I have heard of so many ghostly-goings on around the lanes near Ormskirk over the years, especially on the stretch of road near the mysterious lane where Jimmy and Tony had their terrifying encounters. I cannot offer an adequate explanation, but suspect they may have had something to do with the black witchcraft that was once practised in the area.

Mirages of Murder

On the warm Sunday night of 5 June 1887, a full moon shone down on the elegant Georgian residences of Hamilton Square in Birkenhead. It was almost midnight, and the square was deserted. Police Constable Reid walked into the square on his beat, his measured footsteps echoing over to the recently opened Town Hall. The beat was new and unfamiliar to PC Reid. For the past year he had patrolled the streets of Tranmere, but had been assigned to this beat just three days before. The twenty-minute foot patrol took him around the square, up Cleveland Street and down Duke Street, where he would nod to a colleague on the adjoining beat. Reid would then proceed up Conway Street, and back to Hamilton Square once again.

Upon this humid night, there was no need for the policeman to light his bull's eye lantern, because the silvery light from the full moon in the clear sky was illuminating every street in Wirral. It was even bright enough to read the fine print of a newspaper. PC Reid inspected the square, then headed up Cleveland Street, where he noticed that his colleague, PC Doyle, was talking to a swaying, singing man by a hansom cab. Constable Reid went to see if his assistance was needed, but discovered that PC Doyle was merely bidding goodnight to a wealthy businessman whom he knew by sight. The drunken man had just stepped down from a cab after a night on the town, and was staggering to his residence with his top hat at a crazy angle.

At twenty minutes past midnight, PC Reid entered Hamilton Square again, and immediately noticed a light in the second-floor window of one of the houses. Reid was about to glance away when the distinctive silhouette of a woman's head and shoulders appeared against the drawn curtains of the lit window, and at the same time he heard a bloodcurdling scream. It was very high-pitched, like the shriek of a child, and it definitely came from the direction of the house with the illuminated window. Then PC Reid shuddered when he saw that the silhouetted woman held a knife, and she was plunging it repeatedly into something which was out of sight.

He ran immediately to the house and hammered on the door. After almost two minutes of banging violently on the doorknocker and continuously ringing the bell, a light shone through the semicircular fanlight window over the front door, and a bolt was drawn back behind that door. A feeble, bent old man answered, and the constable pushed him aside and ran up the stairs, two at a time, stumbling in the dark and was soon on the landing. He opened the door of the drawing room, where he guessed the knife-wielding woman would be. It was a beautifully decorated room, with a thick-piled, royal blue carpet decked with roses, luxurious looking furniture, and a huge, fine, crystal chandelier hanging from the high ceiling.

Nothing could have prepared PC Reid for the sight that met his eyes when he opened the door to that drawing room. He had never seen anything as gruesome in all his fourteen years of service. Sitting in a wine-coloured padded easy chair, was a long-haired woman in a voluminous, full-length white nightgown, which was heavily bloodstained. The woman was staring straight at PC Reid with wide, mad-looking eyes, and she held a long bread knife in her lap. On the floor, was the severed head of a girl of about two years of age, and scattered about the room, were other bloody parts of the butchered child.

The woman screamed, and simultaneously leaped out of the chair and charged at him with the knife in her hand. Quick as a flash, the constable pulled the door shut, and he heard the sound of the blade being stabbed against the door panels. By now, the old butler who had admitted Reid was climbing the stairs as quickly as his old bones would allow, and he too heard the woman screaming and furiously stabbing the door in the drawing room. PC Reid suddenly noticed that there was a small brass bolt on the door, and he slid it across, effectively locking the murderous woman in the room. The policeman then told the elderly servant to leave with him, as his life was in danger. The frail old man protested loudly and PC Reid had to almost carry him outside. The policeman then blew hard on his whistle and PC Doyle quickly responded.

As he hurried to Hamilton Square, Doyle flashed his lantern twice to a policeman on the Laird Street beat, and he came running to the square as well. The three policemen went into the house together, and when they entered the drawing room, they found the gas lamps on, as before, but there was no sign of a deranged woman, or any blood, or any signs of a murder.

PC Reid carefully studied the room; the furniture looked the same as it had before, but the blue carpet was now dark green. The old butler, who had wheezed his way back up the stairs, proceeded to tell the officers a strange tale. He said that he was minding the house until his master returned from a month's holiday in Wales, and that over the past fortnight, he had taken to sleeping with plugs of cottonwool in his ears, because of the awful sounds he had heard coming from the drawing room in the dead of night. Another servant had explained to him that the sounds were the wails of a ghostly child who was brutally murdered by the master's mentally ill wife some years ago. Apparently, the body was disposed of in secret and the murder covered up. The master's wife had committed suicide not long afterwards, but her ghost had returned to haunt the house. The master had even had a bolt fitted to the outside of the drawing room door to fasten it at night, because that door had been seen to open of its own accord.

The butler offered the policemen a drink but they were so unnerved by the supernatural tale, that they declined the offer and quickly returned to their beats. The Hamilton Square apparition is just one example of instances where the ghost of a murderer or murder victim repeatedly goes through the motions of ghastly deeds committed long ago.

*

In the fourth volume of Haunted Liverpool I wrote about the phantom strangler of Canning Street – the alarming apparition of a woman at a window who is seen regularly combing her hair in front of a mirror, moments before a pair of hands reach out and grip her neck. Those who have seen the ghostly woman from close quarters maintain that a pillowcase is put over her head by the hands, which later throttle and shake her before the whole appalling scene vanishes.

Observers of this murderous mirage from the past have truly believed that they were witnessing a real crime, and have alerted the police, only to later learn that they had actually witnessed a supernatural incident.

In the early 1960s, scores of people in Bootle saw the ghost of a smart-looking, bowler-hatted man who had been murdered in the area several years before, strolling up Strand Road. The man was Harry Baker, a well known credit-draper, or 'clubman', whose battered body had been found at High Leigh, near Knutsford in June 1958. Alas, no clues were forthcoming from the sightings of Baker's ghost, and the murder case is still classed as unsolved.

Sharona

In 2000, sixty-year-old Keith lay at death's door in the Royal Liverpool Teaching Hospital on Prescot Road. Keith had an advanced form of pancreatic cancer, and his condition was regarded as terminal. He had undergone chemotherapy, but the treatment had merely lengthened the months of suffering, by temporarily retarding the growth, and now Keith lay on his own in a room in the hospital with a rosary and crucifix around his neck and a bottle of holy water on his bedside cabinet – his religious sister's desperate attempts at curing her brother's dreadful condition.

Keith was the father of three children, grandfather of two, and also had three sisters and two brothers. His wife had divorced him almost twenty years before, and Keith was currently living with a woman in the Walton area of Liverpool. Keith had told all his relatives that he wanted to die alone and in peace. In particular, he had told his partner Joan that he wanted her to stay away from the hospital because he didn't want to upset her by dying before her eyes, as it would be too traumatic for her.

Drifting in and out of consciousness from the effects of morphine and co-codamol, Keith found the fantasy world of dreams overlapping with reality. A huge, six-foot tall cat with black and yellow stripes sat in front of the door to the private room. Its large, green, human-like eyes narrowed as its mouth curled up and smiled, just like the Cheshire Cat of Lewis Carroll's Wonderland tale. Keith squeezed his eyes shut then looked back at the cat, only to find the giant feline had evaporated, yet it had seemed so real for a phantasm of the mind.

Keith's fevered eyes gazed up at the ceiling, only to behold the mind-bending sight of a gigantic clock-face with twirling hands set in a dark purple sky across which a succession cumulus clouds were skudding. The white, clinical-looking ceiling had gone, and the colossal clock-face, with its wildly spinning hands, was falling down towards Keith, who was paralysed with fear – his only means of escape being to close his eyes to the surreal and menacing timepiece. Keith braced himself for a collision, but the gargantuan dial didn't flatten him, instead he was suddenly greeted with a strange peaceful silence. Then came the sound of a wind buffeting his ears, and it whistled faintly around him. All about him there were cobweb-like filaments of phosphorescent material, drifting in a black starry void. Now and then, Keith caught glimpses of the hospital room, and was even aware of a nurse entering and inspecting the saline drip which was plumbed to his wrist, but she looked translucent, almost like the x-rayed image of a human.

A soft, small hand clasped his, and Keith turned to see a girl whom he surmised to be another vision of his drugged mind. She was exceptionally beautiful, and aged about seventeen or eighteen. Her hairstyle and clothes belonged to the 1950s, and her face was tantalisingly familiar, but who was she? The angelic powdered panstick face, the dark green eyes, and the girl's innocent endearing smile were like something from a half-remembered recurring dream. Then in a flash he remembered who this girl was, and his heart fluttered. It was Sharona McDonald, his first ever real girlfriend from the most exciting period of his life, the golden age of rock n' roll, way back in the Fifties. Nineteen-fifty-eight to be exact – the rip-roaring age of the Teddy Boy which atom-blasted the dusty big band culture to smithereens. Crooners in cardigans trembled when the lads in their square cut jackets and bootlace ties invaded the dance halls to jive the night away. At sweet sixteen, Keith had queued with hundreds of others in Lime Street to see *Black Board Jungle* at the Scala Cinema. He had danced in the cinema aisles to the music of Bill Haley and his Comets singing *Rock Around the Clock*, and outside that picture house so long ago, he first beheld the beautiful Sharona.

At Bill's Café, at the top of Paddington, Keith and Sharona drank milkshakes or coffee, and danced to the jukebox hits. Keith dated her for three years – and how amazing those years were – the best years of his life. Tragically, Sharona died in a traffic accident on the East Lancs Road in the winter of 1960, and Keith's world also died in that car crash on that snowy morning. So this had to be either a cruel trick of a fevered, drugged mind, or perhaps some long-buried subconscious wish-fulfilment.

A howling noise swooshed through Keith's body, and he looked at Sharona in fear. Had his time come at last?

"It's just the astral wind, don't be afraid, Keith," said Sharona in a soft, reassuring voice, and she gently squeezed his hand.

The hospital bed and room materialised and slowly came back into focus, but seemed to be illuminated by an ethereal silvery light which certainly did not come from the drab neon ceiling lights.

"Come on, Keith," whispered Sharona, leading her boyfriend from the bed and straight through the wall into the corridor. They rode the elevator to the ground floor, and during the journey, Keith noticed a tall black figure dressed in a strange costume – similar to a nun's habit – but devoid of any colour, or even a face. When Sharona saw this sinister figure, she quickly led Keith away from it, and he had the feeling that the eerie black entity was some personification of the Grim Reaper.

Sharona shepherded Keith out of the hospital and down the road. He suddenly "felt non-existent and vaporous". Then, in an instant, Keith found himself in some crowded place where rock n' roll music was booming. He felt like a teenager again, and was surrounded by Teddy boys and their girls on every side. Before him was Sharona, dancing to *Bonie Moronie*. Keith couldn't be sure, but the place seemed to be the Blue Ball pub which he and Sharona had often visited on Saturday nights with many other young rock n' rollers. How could that be? The Blue Ball was demolished in the 1970s to make way for the hospital he had just left. The dancing went on for a long time, and when Keith caught a glimpse of himself in the pub mirror, he saw that he was dressed in the height of Ted fashion, with a scarlet square-cut drape jacket, bootlace tie and 'brothel-creeper' shoes. His hair was slicked back with the top combed to a pointed fringe. It must have taken months to grow the sideburns he sported in that looking glass, and how young and cool he looked.

Eddie Cochran's *Come On Everybody* suddenly erupted from the loudspeakers and it was followed by *Move It* by Cliff Richard. Then came the last dance – the 'slowy' – and of course, that dance was with his beloved Sharona. During the intimate minutes with his long-dead sweetheart, he confronted her about her true nature, and whether the Blue Ball was just a dying man's dream, but what Sharona told him was not what he had expected at all.

"I'm not dead, just out of sight, Keith," she told him. "All of the dead are like this, out of sight and mostly out of mind. Like a baby when it's in the womb, before it's in this world."

"Am I dead?" Keith asked, and he hoped he was, because from what he was experiencing, death was not at all bad.

"No, but you've crossed over here and you'll be going back soon," said Sharona, and a small tear welled in the corner of her eye.

"What do you mean, 'going back'?"

Keith hugged his first and last love, and clung on to her tightly, so scared of losing her to that infinite void of wailing astral winds from where she had first come to him. "I don't want to let you go, Sharona. Please stay!" he sobbed.

"When you get back, and when you get better, remember that I'm still around, even though you can't see me," Sharon told him, and now she was crying too. "Go to that shop where you sold all your records, Keith, and when you get them back, play them, and I'll be there with you."

"I will …"

Keith felt faint again, and a thick fog developed before his eyes. The last thing he felt was the tiny, soft hand of Sharona gently slipping from his. He awakened in his bed, and through some miracle that we clueless mortals call remission, the tide of his ailing health started to turn.

Three months later he was allowed to go home, because the cancer had cleared. Haunted by Sharona's plea to get back the old records, Keith went to the secondhand shop in Kensington and bought back his box of old seventy-eights, thirty-threes and forty-fives. He then sat in his bedroom, playing the records, and he suddenly knew that Sharona was there, because he smelt his sweetheart's old perfume, 'Evening In Paris'.

"Sharona, I promise, you'll never be out of my mind," Keith whispered.

Other Titles Published by The Bluecoat Press